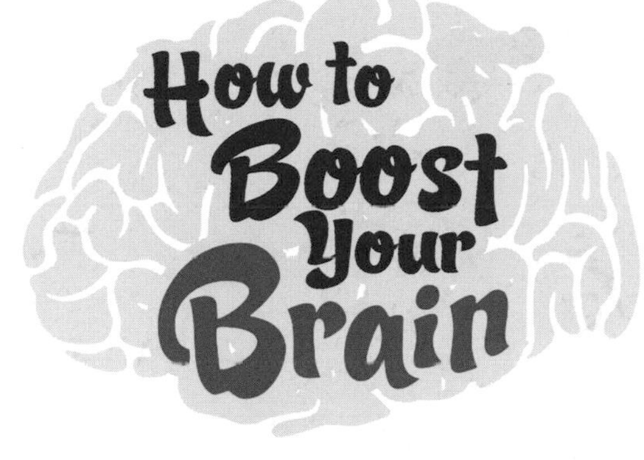
How to
Boost
Your
Brain

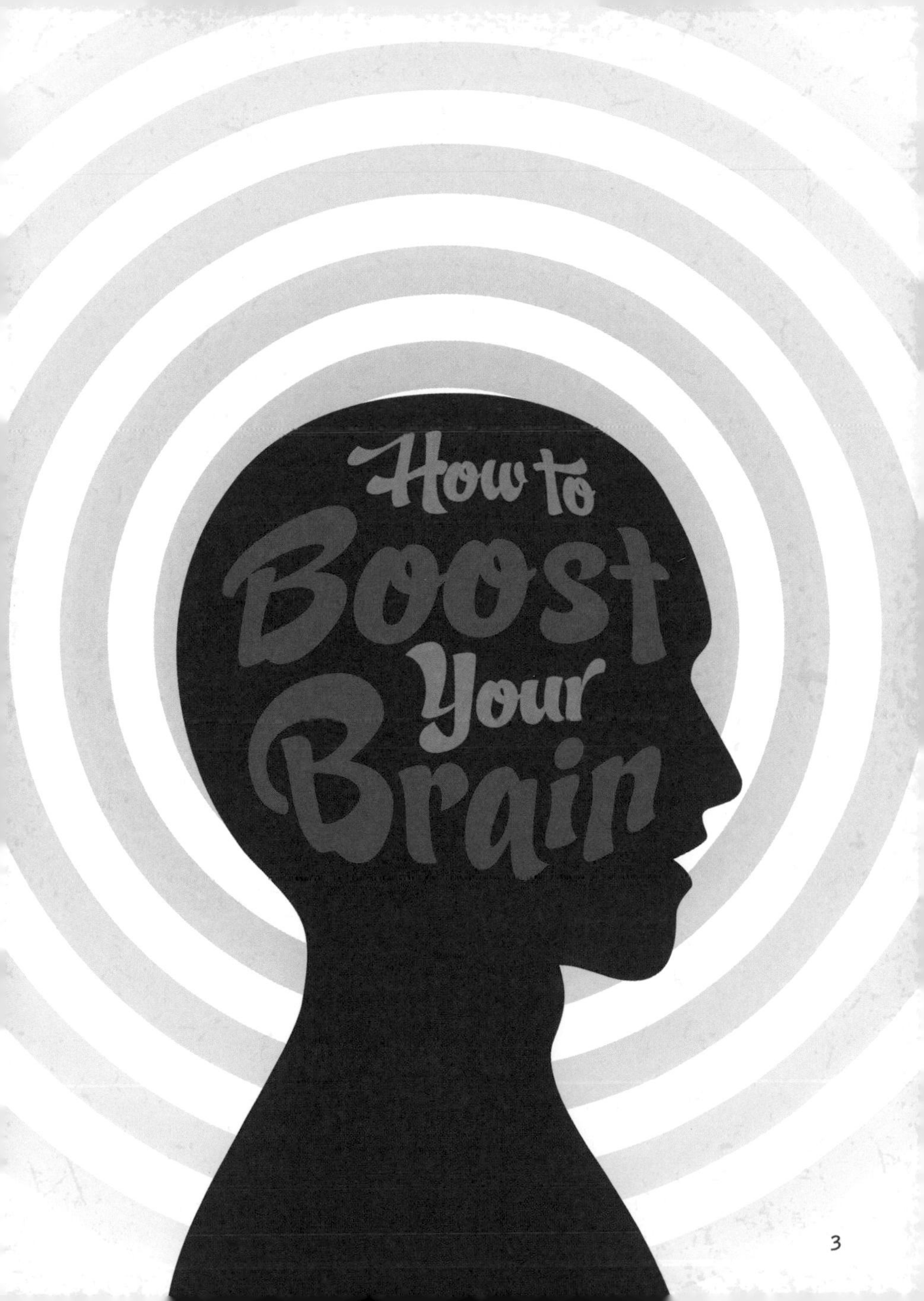
How to
Boost
Your
Brain

First published in the United Kingdom by Lakeland in 2013

Packaged by Susanna Geoghegan

Printed in China

SUCCESS IS NOT FINAL, FAILURE IS NOT : IT IS THE COURAGE TO CHANGE THAT KEEPS US GROWING...

CONTENTS >>

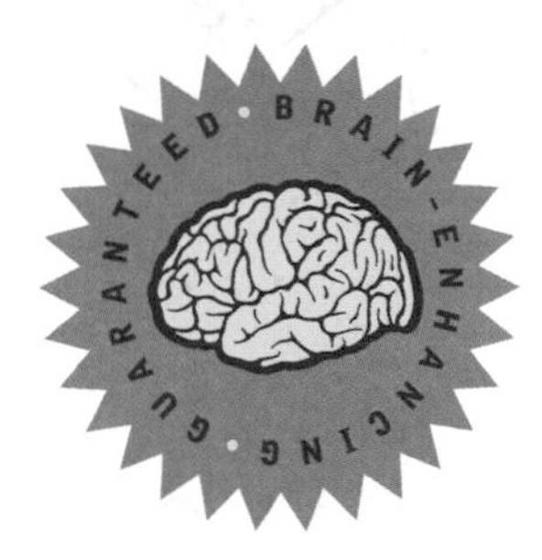

GUARANTEED · BRAIN-ENHANCING ·

Introduction

Much of what this book offers is possible because of the brain's extraordinary adaptive ability – its neuroplasticity. The chemistry and architecture of the human brain is constantly changing and forming new connections between brain cells, allowing those that are rarely used to fade away, even making new brain cells, so it's never too late to boost your brain, master new skills, create fresh perspectives and generate better outcomes in your life.

How to Boost Your Brain

Scientists used to think that most of the neural pathways are laid down during early childhood and that adulthood is a downward slide into faculty failure as brain cells die and neural connections with them. Fortunately during the last decade this view has been replaced by a more fluid model. Now all areas of the brain are considered to be plastic, even after childhood. This is great news because it means that we're never too old to develop our brains, and to modify our experience of the world.

A newborn baby has an estimated 100 billion nerve cells (neurons) which are bombarded with new information, because everything is new. At birth our genes have predetermined a neural roadmap with which the brain works, but the finer details are shaped by the environmental input and by the finer connections made between neurons which are always developing and changing despite your genetics or your age.

Brain cells die every day, but unless you suffer from a neural wasting disease or you abuse drugs, this figure is still minute compared to how many you have left. So concentrate on keeping physically and mentally active, exposing yourself to new, fun and challenging experiences every day to take proper care of your plastic brain.

At birth each neuron has about 2,500 connections, but most of the brain's wiring happens afterwards and continues into adulthood. During the first few months of a baby's life the brain makes a surplus of neural connections and by the age of three each neuron has about 15,000 synapses – points of connection with other neurons. This number decreases in adulthood because connections which are rarely used fade away in a process known as "synaptic pruning" – the brain retains those "useful" connections that are being reinforced by daily use. However, new neural connections can be made as well as existing ones strengthened to generate even more synapses. That's why multisensory learning is so effective because it makes more connections and that's why what you do today influences the way you think and feel tomorrow.

We're never too old to develop our brains, and to modify our experience of the world

Throughout this book a key at the top of the page indicates which areas of experience are targeted in each topic. Most of the terms – Physical, Emotional, Spiritual, Sensory (the five senses) and Creative – are fairly obvious, but you may not be familiar with the other three. The Limbic System is a set of brain structures involved in emotion, behaviour and long-term memory; Proprioception is the awareness of where your body parts, and especially your limbs, are in space; Metacognition refers to knowing about knowing, thinking about thinking.

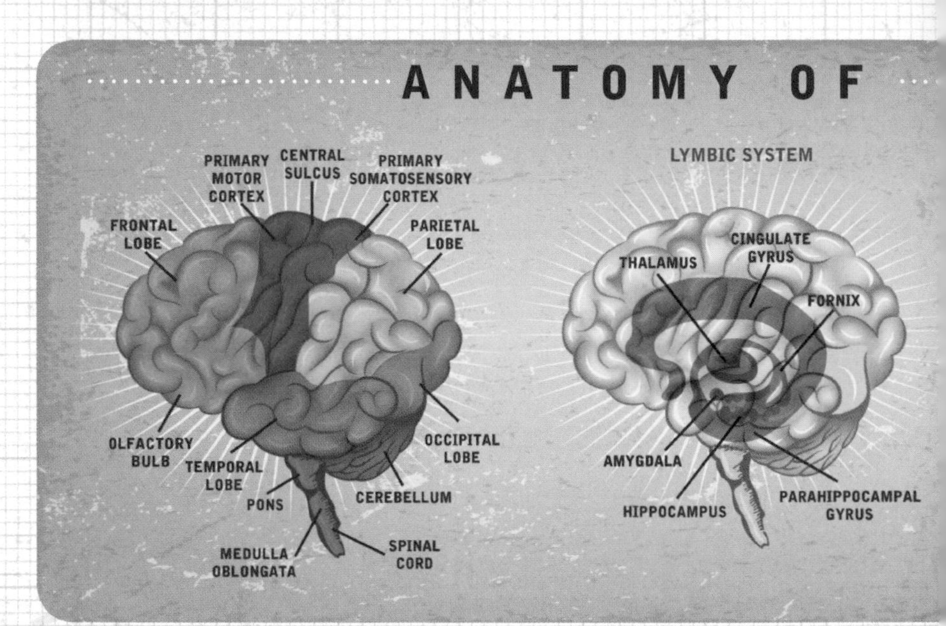

FRONTAL LOBE >
Responsible for emotions and behaviour, the ability to recognize future consequences, choose between good and bad actions, regulate socially acceptable behaviour and spot similarities and differences between things and events. Also involved with long-term memory associated with emotions.

PARIETAL LOBE >
Spatial awareness and integrating sensory information from various parts of the body, numeric literacy and manipulation of objects.

MOTOR CORTEX >
Planning, control, and execution of voluntary motor functions.

SENSORY CORTEX >
A general term for the cortices of the five senses: visual cortex (occipital lobes), auditory cortex (temporal lobes), somatosensory cortex and gustatory cortex (postcentral gyrus), olfactory cortex (entorhinal and piriform cortices).

OCCIPITAL LOBE >
Visual processing centre housing the visual cortex; local orientation, spatial-frequency, visual recognition of shapes and colours.

THE CEREBRAL CORTEX >
The outer layer of neural tissue 2–4mm thick, made up of six horizontal layers. It plays a key role in memory, attention, perceptual awareness, thought, language and consciousness.

TEMPORAL LOBE >
Hearing, long-term memory, meaning and language, emotion and learning. Contains the hippocampus which processes short-term memories into long-term memories and the amygdala which regulates fear and has a primary role in processing memories with an emotional component.

THE BRAIN

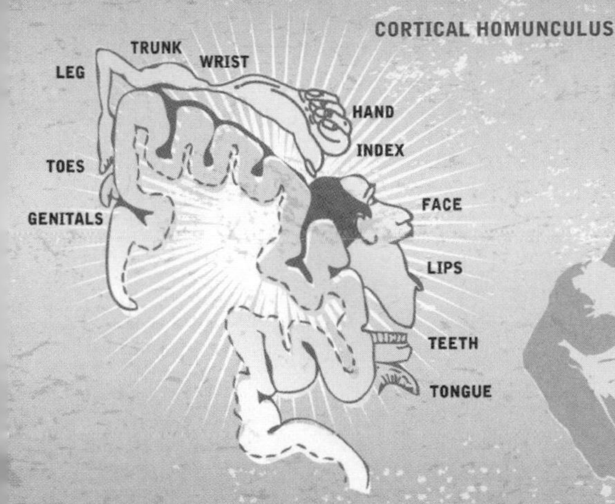

CEREBELLUM >
Controls primarily balance and motor control, but recent research has shown it plays a role in attention, language and mental imagery.

CORPUS COLLOSUM >
The cord that connects the left hemisphere of the brain to the right.

BRAIN STEM >
The oldest part of the brain but very important because the nerve connections from the rest of the brain pass through it down the spinal cord to muscles, skin and other organs. It regulates cardiac and respiratory function, the central nervous system and the sleep cycle and is vital for maintaining consciousness.

THE CORTICAL HOMUNCULUS

In 1870 Eduard Hitzig and Gustav Fritsch used a thin probe to apply electricity to the exposed cerebral cortex of a living dog. Different parts of the body experienced involuntary muscular contractions depending on which part of the cerebral cortex was stimulated, and when they destroyed small areas of the cortex the corresponding body areas became paralyzed. This is how they discovered that each part of the body is controlled by a specific region of the primary motor cortex. However, some body parts like the hands and the tongue use up much more processing space than others, as shown in the diagram above, which is called a cortical homunculus.

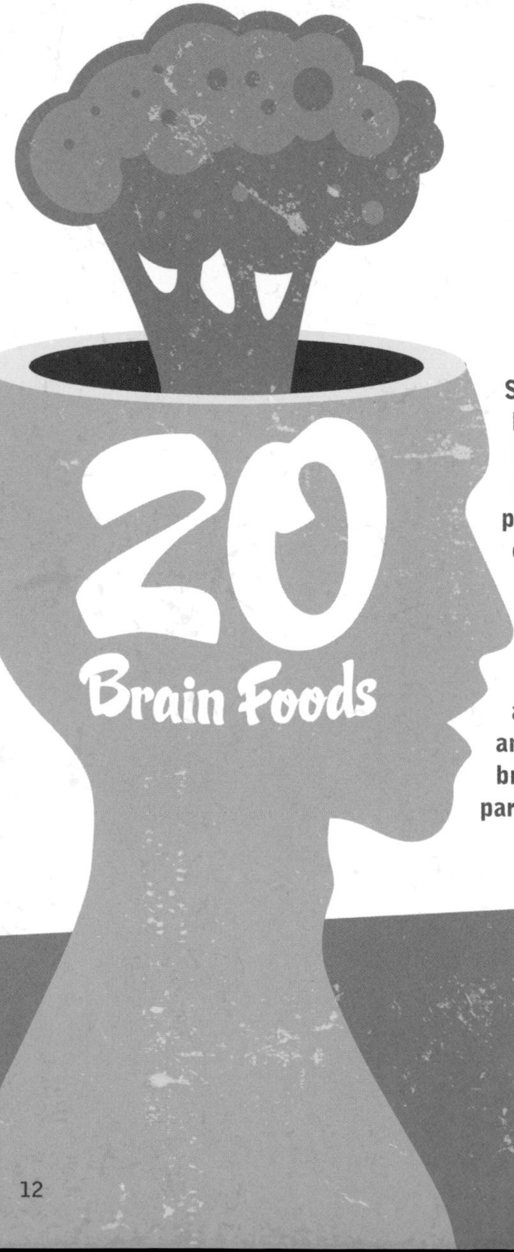

20 Brain Foods

Broccoli is one of the richest vegetable sources of calcium, iron, magnesium and vitamin K, which improves cognition and memory

Study after study has shown that you can improve your concentration, intelligence, alertness and problem-solving ability, and elevate your mood, simply by what mind nutrition you choose to put in your mouth. These twenty foods are rich in essential fats, amino acids, antioxidants, vitamins and minerals that are critical for brain function when used as a part of a healthy balanced diet.

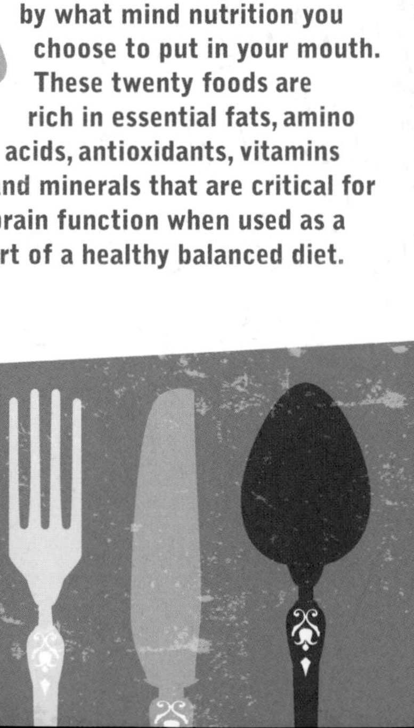

1 WHOLE GRAINS

From porridge and rye bread to brown rice, whole grains are cereal grains that contain germ, endosperm, and bran; refined grains, which should be avoided, retain only the endosperm. Whole grains provide vitamins B6, B12 and B9 (folic acid) and they have a low glycemic index (GI), meaning they take longer to digest, so they release their energy slowly, whereas refined grains have a high GI – they are rapidly absorbed and encourage fluctuations in blood sugar levels. A stable blood sugar level ensures optimum brain function all day long.

2 QUINOA

Quinoa (pronounced "keen-wah") is widely considered the mother lode of whole grains (although it isn't a grain at all and is more closely related to leafy green vegetables like spinach and Swiss chard than grasses); quinoa and soy are the only vegetarian sources of protein that contain all nine essential amino acids. Quinoa is a good source of dietary fibre and phosphorus, magnesium, manganese, copper and iron and it also benefits migraine sufferers.

WALNUTS

Walnuts are a powerhouse for the brain; they contain up to 20 per cent protein, omega-6 and omega-3 fatty acids essential for healthy brain cell membranes, vitamins E and B6, and help maintain healthy levels of the calming neurotransmitter serotonin which influences our moods and appetite.

4 ALMONDS

The magic brain ingredient in almonds is phenylalanine, an essential amino acid involved in the production of the mood stabilizing hormones adrenaline, noradrenaline and dopamine. Almonds are rich in vitamin E and they are also a good source of riboflavin, iron, magnesium and L-carnitine, which supports choline metabolism to improve memory by reducing neuronal degeneration. They also help reduce LDL "bad" cholesterol while preserving the HDL "good" cholesterol.

5 CASHEWS

Cashews contain over eighty nutrients and help increase oxygen flow to your brain. They are high in fibre, protein, iron, magnesium, phosphorus, zinc, copper and manganese and a good source of polyunsaturated and monounsaturated fats. They also contain the essential amino acid tryptophan, which increases levels of serotonin.

6 PECANS

A recent study has shown that pecan nuts protect your brain against motor neuron degeneration. They are rich in vitamin E and a good source of choline, a chemical precursor of the neurotransmitter acetycholine. Pecans provide more than 19 vitamins and minerals including vitamin A, several B vitamins, folic acid, calcium, magnesium, phosphorus and zinc.

7 BLACKCURRANTS, BLUEBERRIES, BLACKBERRIES

Of all the berries these three dark berries are the best. They are cheaper than the much hyped acai berry and contain high levels of antioxidants and vitamin C which protect the brain from free radicals and the oxidative stress involved in many diseases. They have high levels of anthocyanin, the dark purple flavonoid that protects against cancer and heart disease.

8 STRAWBERRIES

Strawberries are one of nature's tastiest and healthiest foods and reduce the risk of developing age-related brain decline. They contain more vitamin C than oranges (half a cup provides seventy per cent of the Recommended Daily Amount) plus a flavonoid called quercetin which inhibits the growth of cancerous cells.

9 FLAX SEEDS (AKA LINSEED)

Flax seeds are the richest known vegetable source of omega-3 fatty acids which help to turn off the stress response to calm us down. Omega-3 deficiency has been linked to postpartum depression, ADHD, Tourette syndrome and chronic fatigue syndrome. They are a good source of fibre, folic acid, vitamin B6, manganese, magnesium, phosphorus and copper.

10 PUMPKIN SEEDS

Pumpkin seeds are high in fibre and protein; they are a rich source of manganese, magnesium, iron, phosphorous, omega-6 and omega-3 fatty acids. A daily handful of pumpkin seeds is a good source of zinc, used in the brain's hippocampus to enhance memory. Zinc is a critical element in human health but a common nutritional deficiency, especially among children.

11 SUNFLOWER SEEDS

Sunflower seeds are rich in mono and polyunsaturated fatty acids and contain several vitamins and minerals including vitamin E, vitamin C, B1, B3, B5, B6, calcium, magnesium, potassium, zinc and selenium. They also contain tryptophan, which helps the brain to produce the calming neurotransmitter serotonin.

12 POMEGRANATE

Pomegranate juice is a fashionable brain food, and with good reason: it contains high levels of antioxidants and folic acid. A recent study at Loma Linda University in California showed that mice fed with the juice were 35 per cent better at navigating mazes, and had fifty per cent less beta-amyloid, a precursor to Alzheimer's disease.

13 TOMATOES

Tomatoes contain high levels of an antioxidant called lycopene which has multiple health benefits, from protection against heart disease and cancer to skin ageing. It is a brain food because it improves memory. Researchers at the University of Kentucky studied a group of elderly Catholic nuns and found that those who consumed at least 30mg of lycopene daily were more physically capable and had clearer memories.

14 BROCCOLI

Broccoli is one of the richest vegetable sources of calcium, iron, magnesium and vitamin K, which improves cognition and memory. It contains high levels of folic acid which helps to break down an amino acid linked to thrombosis and cardiovascular disease called homocysteine.

15 AVOCADO

High in folic acid and healthy monounsaturated fats which help blood flow and the central nervous system, reduce blood pressure, and improve skin and hair health, a quarter of an avocado a day gives you all these benefits without piling on the calories. Vitamin B6 and potassium in avocados can also improve your libido - the Aztecs named the avocado tree *ahuacatl* or "testicle tree".

16 WILD SALMON (NOT FARMED)

Wild salmon isn't cheap but it is an excellent source of choline, a chemical precursor of the neurotransmitter acetycholine which benefits the brain, especially the hippocampus which is responsible for long-term memory and spatial awareness. The omega-3 acids contained in fish oils protect brain nerve cell membranes.

17 EGGS

The humble egg contains high levels of tryptophan and choline and about ten per cent of your daily protein requirement, as well as vitamins D, B2, B5, B9, B12, iodine and phosphorous. It has anti-inflammatory properties and contrary to popular opinion, can improve your cholesterol profile. Two antioxidants in egg yolk called lutein and zeaxanthin guard against macular degeneration and cataracts.

18 GARLIC

Garlic has been used medicinally since the time of the ancient Sumerians, although some eastern yogis argue that garlic is a brain toxin that slows reflexes. It is a good source of selenium and aids blood circulation to improve oxygen flow to the brain. It reduces bad cholesterol and has a powerful antioxidant effect.

19 GREEN TEA

This enhances memory and focus. It contains caffeine, but also catechins and powerful antioxidants called polyphenols which are vital for regulation of glucose and dopamine. The best (and most expensive) is Japanese Matcha – grown in the shade and then stone ground to a fine bright green powder.

20 DARK CHOCOLATE

The cacao bean was revered by the Mayans and Aztecs and its scientific name "theobroma cacao" means food of the gods. Chocolate is stuffed with goodies like magnesium (fifty per cent of people in industrialized countries are magnesium deficient), theobromine (an alkaloid stimulant and chemical relative of caffeine), flavonoids and antioxidants, but only if it contains a high proportion of cacao bean (at least 75 per cent) that hasn't been degraded by over-refining, or over-roasting. The phenylethylamine (PEA) in chocolate increases alertness and well-being – it is the same chemical released by the brain when we are in love.

Ten Brain Enhancers

"To think is to practise brain chemistry."

Deepak Chopra

If you want to have a healthy brain, take good care of it. Here are ten ways to keep it minty fresh...

1 SLEEP

Getting regular quality sleep doesn't just make you feel more alert, it is vital for brain function as well as brain development during infancy and childhood. While you sleep your brain works hard to sift and sort the experiences of the day. Sleep enhances learning and memory. If you spend three hours revising for a test, then sleep for eight hours, you will retain more than if you doubled your exposure to the information by staying awake and revising for a further three hours. Research has found a link between the brain's plasticity and the amount of deep sleep and REM sleep.

2 EXERCISE

The brain needs oxygen and glucose and exercise improves their delivery by strengthening the cardiovascular and circulatory systems. It also stimulates the release of feel-good chemicals – endorphins – which reduce stress. When you exercise you stimulate and strengthen the neural receptors that allow communication between your nerves and muscles. Physical inactivity actually diminishes these receptors. "Use it or lose it" is literally true: muscle activity is key to building and maintaining healthy brain function at a chemical level.

3 LEARN SOMETHING NEW

In the movie *Short Circuit*, the robot Johnny 5 has a memorable catchphrase: "need input". The same applies to your brain – it is a learning machine that thrives on input, and the more new experiences you can feed it, the better your brain function. Learn something new every day – take up a hobby, read a blog, learn a language or musical instrument, take a trip, play a computer game, learn to cook, memorize three new words – anything that gives your brain new data to process.

4 EAT HEALTHY FOOD

Certain foods are brain boosters (see page 12), but a generally healthy diet is vital for good brain function and to help you stay alert. Eat small regular meals to maintain stable blood sugar and never skip breakfast. A poor diet high in sugar and fat and low in vitamins makes you lethargic, affects mood and concentration and actually harms brain cells. So eat healthily for your brain's sake, not just to stay trim.

5 SOCIALIZE

Your brain thrives on company. Socializing is very challenging for the brain, because it requires a lot of cognitive power to interact with others, especially in unfamiliar social situations. Mental decline in old age has been linked to lack of social interaction.

6 ME TIME

Spending quality time in the company of your own thoughts rather than outside stimuli is just as important to brain health and function as socializing and it's not just about de-stressing. Introspection stimulates the prefrontal cortex, and develops metacognition, self-evaluation and decision-making.

7 LEARN THE PIANO

A few years ago the Mozart Effect – playing Mozart to infants and even babies in utero with the aim of raising their IQ – became very fashionable. There's no scientific evidence that listening to music has any effect at all, but learning an instrument in childhood is profoundly beneficial for brain development, especially spatial-temporal intelligence.

Dr Alexandra Lamont of the University of Keele says, "The keyboard seems to be most effective because it's a spatial layout, and music itself is arranged over time, so you have both elements that will help develop spatial-temporal thinking."

8 LAUGHTER

Laughing and humour trigger healthy changes in the body, provide instant stress relief, diminish pain, boost the immune system and improve memory. The physical act of laughing fills the lungs with oxygen, exercises the abdominal and facial muscles, releases neck tension and triggers the release of endorphins to relax the whole body (see page 118).

9 REPLACE BAD HABITS WITH GOOD ONES

Limited and repetitive negative thought patterns and behaviour – bad habits – are one of the major causes of discontent in our lives. We indulge bad habits to make us feel better, but long term they usually have the opposite effect in return for offering a short-term reward. Instead of focusing on eliminating your bad habit, direct your efforts into establishing good mental habits. As you accrue rewards from increasing your positive behaviour you will be less tempted to seek the quick fix rewards of bad habits (see page 98).

10 CHALLENGE YOUR ASSUMPTIONS

Every time we face a challenge we employ a repertoire of assumptions. Up to a point this is natural and essential for survival – assumptions can keep us safe by allowing us to act quickly – but when they are based on faulty or irrational reasoning they limit our opportunities. Most outstanding achievements and inventions were made by people who dared to challenge assumptions – their own, and existing orthodoxies of their time and culture (see page 129).

Ten Brain Drains

These brain drains all have short- and long-term negative effects on the brain. In most cases prolonged exposure leads to irreversible neural damage and brain atrophy.

1 HIGH-FRUCTOSE CORN SYRUP (HFCS)

High-fructose corn syrup is made by passing corn syrup through an enzymatic process to convert some of its glucose to fructose; this makes HFCS six times sweeter than cane sugar (sucrose). Fructose occurs naturally in small quantities in fruit but the detractors of HFCS believe its high levels are responsible for a dramatic rise in obesity and diabetes in the developed world. It has no nutritional value, and disrupts liver function because it isn't broken down during the digestive process like other sugars. This may increase the risk of diabetes and heart disease and make it harder for your body to maintain stable blood sugar levels, which affects the brain. It may also affect the mechanism that tells our brain when we are full, and two recent studies have found high levels of mercury in the product, a poison which also affects brain function. HFCS is added to a lot of processed food, so read ingredient labels carefully, and try to eat fresh unprocessed food whenever possible.

2 ALCOHOL

We all know the effects of having one drink too many – slurred speech, loss of balance, slowed reaction times, loss of inhibitions – so clearly alcohol effects the brain, but over time even modest amounts of alcohol cause serious and persistent changes in the brain as well as brain volume shrinkage and disruption in the growth of new brain cells. Every mood-altering drug affects one or more major neurotransmitters in the brain and alters its reward pathway, but alcohol affects all of them at the same time, causes dehydration and malnutrition and damages cells and synapses. Studies have linked moderate alcohol consumption with a decreased risk of cardiovascular disease, but not so with the brain. The more you drink the more your brain volume diminishes.

3 TELEVISION

Elton John has publicly denounced television as "arse-paralysingly brain crippling" but don't just take his word for it; plenty of scientific evidence shows that TV has harmful effects on the brain, especially in children. It encourages intellectual passivity and deprives the brain of more stimulating experiences; while viewing, brain waves move into an Alpha wave pattern making us more suggestible to advertising and propaganda. For more details on the negative effects of TV on the brain, see page 40.

4 STRESS

In situations of acute stress the release of powerful chemicals like cortisol, adrenaline and noradrenaline into the bloodstream is useful because they raise blood pressure, breathing and heart rate, equipping us to react to danger. However, it takes the sympathetic nervous system a long time to calm down afterwards, and until the body regains equilibrium other functions like growth, reproductive and immune systems are suppressed. Cortisol interferes with the function of neurotransmitters and affects long-term memory. If we remain chronically stressed for a long time our brain function is affected. The cumulative effect of long-term stress injures and kills brain cells in the hippocampus, the part of the brain required for memory and learning.

5 SMOKING

When you inhale, the smoke enters your lungs and nicotine molecules in the tobacco enter the bloodstream and reach the brain within seven seconds, where they attach themselves to a neurotransmitter called acetylcholine. Acetylcholine controls many body functions including muscle movement, blood pressure and heart rate, as well as learning and memory. Blood pressure and heart rate rise, making the smoker feel more alert; smoking also raises levels of dopamine to produce feelings of pleasure and reward. But because nicotine artificially arouses these neurotransmitters, a habitual smoker relies on nicotine to cause this arousal, and feels less able to concentrate without it.

Long term the smoke in the cigarette damages the circulatory system so the brain is deprived of oxygen. It does this in a triple whammy – carbon monoxide damages the protective cells which line blood vessels so that fats and plaque can more readily stick to them, restricting blood flow. Meanwhile, the nicotine actually triggers the release of stored fats into the bloodstream, and also promotes the growth of new blood vessels to feed the fats and plaques that stick to the vessel walls, in a process called vascularization. All this means that oxygen and glucose are delivered less efficiently to every cell in the body, including those in the oxygen-hungry brain.

6 SHARING A BED WITH A PARTNER

Getting a good night's sleep is imperative for optimal brain function; sharing a bed with a partner qualifies as a brain drain because a recent study by Austrian scientists has found that people of both sexes have more disturbed sleep when they share a bed than when they sleep alone, although the perception differs between the sexes.

Professor Gerhard Kloesch and his team studied eight unmarried childless couples in their twenties over twenty nights. Each day the subjects were given cognitive tests, had their stress hormone levels measured and were questioned about how well they thought they had slept. The men said that they had slept better with a partner, but their cognitive tests did not bear this out; women reported feeling more refreshed when sleeping alone, but their stress levels and cognitive abilities did not suffer as much when they slept with a partner. Dr Neil Stanley, a sleep specialist from the University of Surrey, was not surprised by Kloesch's findings: "Historically, we have never been meant to sleep in the same bed as each other . . . sleep is the most selfish thing you can do and it's vital for good physical and mental health."

7 TRANS FATS AND PARTIALLY HYDROGENATED OILS

Your brain is composed of two-thirds fat, so eating the right monounsaturated and polyunsaturated fats is important, but man-made chemically-altered (hydrogenated) vegetable oils called trans fats impair brain function. They are produced by a process called hydrogenation which turns liquid oil into solid fat. During the last fifty years trans fats have been added to lots of processed foods, from sweets, bread and biscuits to ready meals to improve flavour; plus they rancidify more slowly than natural oils. But as well as increasing levels of bad cholesterol and cardiovascular diseases, trans fats also effect the memory and have been linked to a higher risk of Alzheimer's disease.

Experiments at the Medical University of South Carolina (MUSC) found that rats fed on a diet which included trans fats performed five times worse on simple memory tasks than those fed on the same amount of soybean oil (which is high in high in poly- and monounsaturated fats).

8 ASPARTAME

Aspartame is the chemical name for the artificial sweetener present in many foods and diet soft drinks. It is marketed under the brand names NutraSweet, Equal, Spoonful and Equal-Measure and was discovered by accident in 1965 by industrial chemist James Schlatter while working on an anti-ulcer drug. After nearly ten years of objections by neuroscience experts, aspartame was finally approved for food and drink use in the early eighties, and many scientists believe that it has been responsible for a rise in brain disorders ever since, from depression and memory loss to dementia and even schizophrenia.

Aspartame is made up of three chemicals: phenylalanine (50 per cent), aspartic acid (40 per cent) and methanol (10 per cent).

Phenylalanine is an amino acid which occurs naturally in the brain, but artificially increased levels reduce serotonin, leading to mood swings and depression. High levels of phenylalanine are especially dangerous for infants and foetuses. Aspartic acid is another amino acid which occurs naturally in the brain. At low levels it stimulates NMDA receptors (which control synaptic plasticity and memory function) but high levels allow an excess of calcium into the cell causing neural damage and cell death. One of the by-products of aspartame metabolism, diketopiperazine (DKP), has been linked to an increased risk of brain tumours. Methanol (aka wood alcohol) is highly toxic and probably most familiar to you as anti-freeze.

9 SKIPPING MEALS

Skipping meals to lose weight or for lack of time is a good way to ensure that your brain functions below its best. The brain requires a continuous supply of glucose from the blood; hunger causes low blood sugar levels. When you do finally eat, blood sugar levels spike, causing your body to produce insulin to cope with demand. The result is irritability, foggy thinking, and poor memory function. Eat small meals and healthy snacks throughout the day to maintain stable sugar levels – a constant supply of brain fuel.

10 OBESITY

Several recent studies have shown a link between obesity and dementia. There are a number of possible factors: obesity exacerbates sleep apnoea, which can starve the brain of oxygen and cause brain damage; it is linked to high blood pressure, heart disease and diabetes, all of which increase brain atrophy. Obesity disrupts production of the hormone Leptin which is secreted by fat cells and plays a central role in fat metabolism leading to increased risk of Alzheimer's. Obesity also causes chronic inflammation of the brain, another cause of brain impairment.

De-Stress

Stress undermines your performance on many levels: emotional, interpersonal and cognitive. It is usually caused by your reaction to external factors, fears, high anxiety, doubts about the future. Here are some ways to reduce the stress in your life...

1 REDUCE THE INPUT REACHING YOUR BRAIN: VISUAL, AUDITORY AND EVEN TACTILE

Simply spending a few minutes in the dark and quiet away from outside disturbances will help the stress to flow away. Too often we seek relaxation in pursuits that hype us up even more.

2 STOP PATHOLOGIZING YOUR LIFE OR TO USE THE VERNACULAR – SHIT HAPPENS, DEAL WITH IT

Life is often uncertain, untidy, muddled and unpredictable. That's normal and so are the good times when you feel happy, healthy and positive. Charlotte Davis Kasl, author of *Finding Joy: 101 Ways to Free Your Spirit and Dance with Life* advises, "Peace of mind comes from not attaching a great deal of significance to either state. We simply note our moods and physical state and gently move toward balance as best we can, accepting it as part of the flow of life."

3 STRESS IS OFTEN THE RESULT OF THINGS WORKING OUT DIFFERENTLY TO HOW WE EXPECT

The best way to prevent this is to practise non-attachment. This doesn't mean disengaging from life or walking around with emotional paralysis, nor is it a fatalistic acceptance of pain; stop fixating on your desires so you can be more flexible and resilient when things don't go to plan. The next time your delivery pizza arrives without mushrooms, slow down, breathe deeply for thirty seconds and allow yourself a better response than reflexive stress, frustration or anger; when good things happen, just enjoy them rather than stress about trying to prolong them.

4 MOVE AROUND AND STRETCH

If you're not a fan of exercise you don't want to be told what you already know – that exercise reduces stress – but even if you still can't be bothered to get active, at least do some stretches or take a walk round the block. If you feel like death after spending eight hours sitting at you computer you've only got yourself to blame.

5 DON'T ALLOW YOUR PAST TO RUIN YOUR PRESENT AND YOUR FUTURE

Live in the moment (see page 52) and accept that change is normal part of life (see page 32). Learn to meditate (see page 112), laugh (see page 118), get adequate sleep (see page 88), eat healthily (see page 12) and de-clutter (see page 136) – don't reinvent the wheel, but don't ignore it either otherwise your most basic needs won't be met.

6 GAIN PERSPECTIVE

Carol Kauffman, assistant clinical professor at Harvard Medical School and director of its Coaching and Positive Psychology Initiative says the best way to stop anxiety and stress from affecting your performance is to gain perspective and be realistic rather than imagine the worst: "I'll ask my patients, 'Are you personally in danger? Are your finances at risk? How can you deal with what's actually on your plate, as opposed to what you see on other people's plates? How can you find the areas where you can take charge?" "She has developed a technique called "rapid-fire disputing" – quickly finding three thoughts that prove your fears unfounded.

7 RECALL YOUR SUCCESSES

The next time you are daunted by a challenge, reduce your anxiety by recalling your successes. What did you do last time that worked, or if you have never faced this situation before, what's the nearest thing that you accomplished and how did that feel?

8 FOCUS ON WHAT YOU CAN DO RATHER THAN WHAT YOU THINK YOU CAN'T

Instead of focusing on the worst possible outcome (WPO), write down the best possible outcome (BPO) followed by the steps you can take to move towards it. Then get busy doing it. Just starting will reduce your anxiety about the WPO because you're already moving towards the BPO.

9 DO A PILE OF IRONING

Deb Shapiro, meditation teacher and co-author of *Be the Change: How Meditation Can Transform You and the World* believes that the repetitive back-and-forth motions of ironing have a calming effect and that it has a lot in common with meditation. "When done with awareness, what is often considered boring and mundane work can actually be a way to develop a quiet and stress-free mind."

10 DANCE IN THE RAIN

The next time the heavens open, don't brace yourself against the elements. Instead, open up your body and have a shower dance. You'll be amazed how this simple act – changing your customary response to an external stimulus – can be transformative in other areas of your life as well.

11 TAKE A STAYCATION

Why subject yourself to the stress and expense of travelling far away to spend a week "relaxing" when you can stay at home and have all the home comforts, lots of day trips and dine out in style? You can spend relaxing quality time with your loved ones, without having to put the dog in kennels, hire a car and get vaccinations.

12 BEAT THE GUILT BY TACKLING SOMETHING THAT HAS BEEN LEFT UNDONE

It might be something small like taking the dog for a walk, replacing the sealant around the bath or emailing a recipe you promised someone two weeks ago, or something major like apologizing or offering forgiveness. Reducing guilty feelings is one of the best ways to de-stress and clear your conscience.

HOW TO HANDLE Change

Change is an inescapable part of the human condition, which is why it has been an important theme for artists and writers throughout history. In his poem "Mutability", Percy Bysshe Shelley says: "Man's yesterday may ne'er be like his morrow; Nought may endure but Mutability." Remind yourself that change happens to everyone and you aren't alone...

1 **All growth involves change and all change can lead to growth if you allow it.** Look for the opportunities that change offers. When you look back and try to pinpoint key events and decisions in your past that have led to better things in your present, they all involve uncomfortable change.

2 **It's easy to feel serene when everything is going your way, but the true test of character comes with hardship.** You cannot change the past, but you can control how you interpret the situation as you face the present challenge. It is vital that your internal dialogue is positive and looks to the future, rather than self-indulgent and either stuck in the past or the imagined future that has been snatched away.

3 **You choose how to react.** Either way you will make it through, but how much better it is to look back and see that you made a conscious choice to act with dignity and grace rather than feel corrosive regret about your bitterness and anger.

4 **It will probably get worse before it gets better.** Change can take a long time, so don't expect instant results. If the change is self-imposed, such as a diet, accept that lasting results won't come immediately.

5 **The external event that caused the change (such as a bereavement or a redundancy) is out of your control, but there are plenty of opportunities for taking action as you plan how to move forward.** "There is good in every situation, no matter how bad" may seem like a platitude, but while looking for the positive may take extraordinary effort at a difficult time, it is the best way to move beyond your instinct to curl up under a duvet and disengage from the world.

6 **Communicate with others.** Talk about your feelings and ask for help. Admitting your failings and drawing on the support of friends and family not only helps you move forward, but it gives those people an opportunity to show their affection by helping you. People like to help – it makes them feel good. So use this period of change to reach out to those you love.

7 **Get good sleep, eat and drink healthily and avoid mood-altering drugs.** You need to access all your resources to handle change rather than stagnate and wallow in emotional comforters.

8 **Find a way to respond to change with humour.** Discovering the humour and absurdity of a situation affords a healthy distance. Laughter helps you cope better with pain, reduces stress, and improves your immune system and well-being. Negative emotions may feel like pragmatism, but they are as unhelpful as walking in a circle while beating yourself with a stick.

The Endorphin Effect

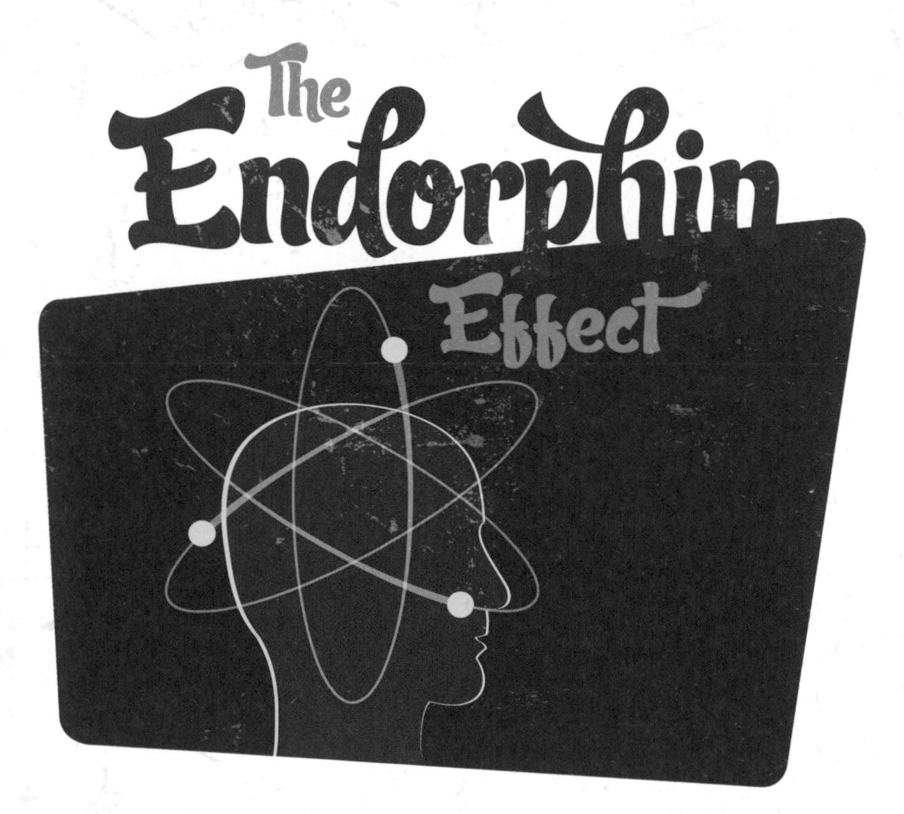

Endorphins are produced naturally by everybody and as well as killing pain they provide pleasure and well-being and are vital for good health. When you make love or feel a great rush of euphoria after winning a race or surviving a dangerous situation, endorphins are responsible. The clue is in the name – "endorphin" combines two words: "endogenous" (produced or growing from within) and "morphine" (a potent opiate analgesic).

Endorphins function as neurotransmitters and are produced by the pituitary gland (a pea-sized structure located at the base of the brain) and above it the hypothalamus (even smaller) during exercise, excitement, pain and lovemaking. Dr William Bloom, one of the world's leading holistic teachers, has devised a technique that can be used to encourage the body to produce endorphins at will to enhance physical and psychological health. He calls it "The Endorphin Effect" and his book of the same name teaches this "simple and accessible method that people can use without effort whenever they want".

Bloom's technique is based on the principle that endorphins can be produced by particular emotional and mental triggers; he teaches how to find and use these triggers, and then suggests a further range of strategies to maximize their effect. He believes that "absolutely anyone – regardless of time, mood or previous experience – can create well-being and build a lasting foundation for all other forms of personal development".

STRAWBERRIES

He encourages his students to make lists of "Strawberries" which he defines as "anything or any thought that brings you pleasure, makes you smile, opens your heart and makes you feel good about life". He advises breaking them down into Places; People, pets and animals; Activities; Peak experiences; Religious figures and symbols; Textures, scents, tastes, sounds and colours.

Next he introduces "The Essential Strawberry Exercise" which is the gateway to triggering endorphins and involves pausing to notice and acknowledge the strawberries in your life. The strawberries can then be used to cultivate the "inner smile" – a method for "communicating safety, reassurance and pleasure down into the physical body" which stimulates the release of endorphins.

Bloom is well known for his clear, practical and friendly style of teaching. One of the strengths of his method is that it is grounded and accessible. The Endorphin Effect is deeply personal and empowering because everybody has different strawberries, which can be as ordinary as stroking a cat or listening to a piece of music, so the technique is easily incorporated into daily life and helps to demystify spiritual well-being. If you want to experience the benefits of this inspirational programme, read his book and test-drive his engaging insights first hand.

It seems everyone is searching for the secret to work harder, faster and longer, but before we dive into our top twelve productivity busters, let's take a look at an important principle that highlights the relationship between speed and productivity.

Imagine you have to reach somewhere sixty miles away and you want to arrive there within an hour. The first half of the motorway journey is hellish – you are stuck in traffic and it takes you forty-five minutes to drive thirty miles. How fast will you have to travel to reach your destination within one hour? You've got fifteen minutes left to drive thirty miles, so you must maintain a speed of 120 mph. That's illegal, dangerous and stressful. However, if you travel at 70 mph, you'll still get there in 25 minutes. You'll only be ten minutes later than scheduled, without risking lives.

The best way to improve an outcome is to set yourself a realistic goal (arrival in 75 minutes, to allow for possible delays) and keep a steady pace. Your top priority should be to identify and eliminate the time-wasting elements of your working day, so you can maintain a steady pace throughout the day, rather than shoot off at double speed, which will only tire you out, increase mistakes and reduce your productivity in the long run.

1 *Eliminating delays and distractions is preferable to increasing speed later to compensate for them.*

2 *Make a start.* Even the most daunting task seems more manageable if you just begin. Then your activity is focused on getting the job done rather than finding ever more inventive distractions to take your mind off the consequences of failure.

3 *If other commitments are playing on your mind, write them down and set the list aside for later, so you can focus on a single task.* Studies show that multitasking is less efficient than doing one thing at a time. Cognitive scientist Dr Pascale Michelon says, "Dividing attention results in less attentional power devoted to all the different tasks that you are trying to do at the same time . . . The result is more errors and waste of time. Although we all have the feeling that multitasking saves us time, it is often not the case."

4 *Take regular breaks.* Set a timer for 45 minutes and then give yourself a ten minute break, move around and stretch your legs. However, if your willpower if flagging, don't use break-taking as an excuse for prevarication (see page 123).

5 *Tackle your most challenging tasks at your most productive time.* For most people this is first thing in the morning.

6 *Keep asking yourself, "Am I making the best use of my time here?"*

7 *Enjoy the process but don't lose sight of your goals.* It's great to get in the zone and enjoy a task, but the Pareto principle (also known as the 80-20 rule) states that roughly 80 per cent of the effects come from 20 per cent of the causes, so always keep in mind whether your activity is advancing your goals (see 6).

8 *Give yourself a reward when you complete a task.*

9 *Fix problems rather than complain about them.* Often this takes less time and is less stressful.

10 *Don't worry about making mistakes, or you won't even be able to begin.* Worrying will lead to more mistakes, not fewer.

11 *Only spend time, energy and attention on things you CAN control.*

12 *Identify a top idea so that when your mind wanders (e.g. when you're in the shower) it ruminates on that idea rather than something negative, useless or trivial.* Paul Graham, founder of venture fund company Y Combinator, explains: "I think most people have one top idea in their mind at any given time. That's the idea their thoughts will drift toward when they're allowed to drift freely. And this idea will thus tend to get all the benefit of that type of thinking, while others are starved of it. Which means it's a disaster to let the wrong idea become the top one in your mind."

HOPE IS LIKE A Goat

Sometimes we all need a creative kick start, something external that helps us to think in a different way. Similes are an effective way to challenge your mind to make connections between two seemingly unconnected ideas...

If you google "simile generator" you will find lots of sites that throw up interesting similes. Some allow you to input your own initial noun, and then give you another. Your job is to get busy making the connection. For example, if you visit *http://www.writingfix.com/right_brain/Serendipitous_Simile_Prose1.htm* you'll find one of the twenty-one interactive word games presented at the original WritingFix in-service sponsored by the Northern Nevada Writing Project. There are two buttons labelled "Human trait" and "Interesting noun"; press the buttons to reveal the pair, then use your imagination to make the connection, and add an adjective to qualify the simile even further.

Suppose the generator returns the results "dream" and "lighthouse": you could write a sentence "His/Her dream was like a lighthouse". This might lead you to imagine a dream as being protective, standing lonely on a storm-beaten outcrop, guiding thoughts away from the rocks. Now add an adjective, your own or a randomly generated one. See *http://watchout4snakes.com/CreativityTools/RandomWord/RandomWordPlus.aspx* where you can generate nouns, adjectives, interjections, adverbs and prepositions of varying complexity from common to obscure. Our "common" search returned the adjective "Overdue".

"Her dream was like an overdue lighthouse guiding thoughts away from the rocks, but too long awaited, an unpaid utility bill . . . etc."

See how quickly a randomly generated simile can get you thinking and writing imaginatively?

TURN OFF YOUR Television

Does the increasing amount of time that we "waste" watching television deprive us of more brain-nourishing activities, or is it something intrinsic in the viewing experience that does the damage? The answer is both.

A normal alert brain generates primarily Beta and Gamma waves, but studies show that within a few minutes of watching television the predominant brain wave pattern is Alpha – associated with relaxation, suggestibility, drowsiness and even hypnosis. You might think this is a good thing, since most people watch TV to relax, but this is the worst state to inhabit while exposed to advertising, news, indeed any TV programme, which promotes the values and beliefs of the makers and producers.

Repeated exposure to TV reinforces this Alpha state. If your brain is accustomed to spending five hours a day (the average daily viewing in US and UK households) watching TV, it struggles to generate other patterns. It might help you get off to sleep in the evening, but it is detrimental to your higher brain functioning.

The left brain, responsible for critical thinking, switches off when we watch TV, making us receptive to mind-programming. As Jim Morrison said in *American Prayer*, "Do you know we are ruled by TV?". When we watch TV there is very little analysis of incoming information and our emotional response becomes desensitized, not only to violence but to things that should arouse compassion – repeated viewing of victims of famine and civil war in Third World countries are a clear example.

TV AND CHILDREN

Children are especially vulnerable to TV exposure because their brains develop faster than those of adults. Studies show that exposing children under the age of 2 to TV is very damaging, and higher levels of TV viewing corresponds to lower academic performance, especially reading ability. Shows like *Sesame Street* are good learning tools for children aged three and above, but they can be detrimental to younger children. Dr Dimitri Christakis says, "*Sesame Street* wasn't designed for kids that young, but it's watched by kids that young because parents think if it's good for a three-year-old, it's good for a two-year-old." Young children do not engage with TV, even educational programmes, the way they do with the real world.

TV viewing is linked to increased levels of Attention Deficit Disorder and poor behaviour, and it isn't just because bad parenting leads to using the TV as a babysitter. Experiments by Herbert Krugman of the Advertising Research Foundation have led him to describe TV viewing as a "sleeping awake" activity.

THE MULLHOLLAND EXPERIMENT

In his famous experiment in the early 1970s Dr Thomas Mulholland was the first scientist to detect a physical reaction to television. He used an electroencephalograph (EEG) machine to measure the brain activity of ten children while they were watching their chosen favourite programmes. He expected to detect high levels of Beta waves, since the children were engaged and excited, but instead he measured predominantly Alpha waves associated with minimal brain activity.

The immune system is immensely complex, so we don't fully understand all the mechanisms that contribute to it; however there is plenty you can do to boost your immunity and ward off illness.

1. **MAINTAIN HEALTHY PH LEVELS.** Your body functions best when the blood is slightly alkaline – a reading of anywhere between 6.75–7.0+ for saliva and 7.5 for urine is normal (you can buy pH testing strips from most chemists). Pathogens thrive in an acidic environment, and many people eating a Western diet have more acidic pH levels but you can restore the balance by eating lost of raw fruit and vegetables. Lemon is an acidic food which is very alkalizing to the body, so drinking a glass of water twice a day with the juice of half a lemon will boost your immune system and provide antioxidants and vitamins too.
2. **GET A GOOD NIGHT'S SLEEP** (see page 88) and make some of the brain foods on page 12 a daily part of your diet.
3. **DRINK AT LEAST EIGHT GLASSES OF WATER A DAY.** This helps your liver and kidneys to flush out the toxins that stress the body.

4 **CUT DOWN ON COFFEE** and caffeinated drinks especially fizzy drinks, which dehydrate.

5 **EXERCISE REGULARLY.** This releases endorphins and improves blood flow and delivery of oxygen to all the cells in your body; however, too much exercise damages the immune system, so avoid overtraining by allowing your body plenty of time to recover.

6 **CUT DOWN** on refined carbohydrates and refined sugars.

7 **MANAGE STRESS** (see page 28). In the short term stress can actually boost the immune system, but persistent chronic stress weakens the immune response and it becomes less responsive. The white blood cell count of people with chronic stress is lower than normal, which makes them more vulnerable to pathogens.

8 **TAKE COLD SHOWERS.** Scientists in Prague immersed a group of young men in water at 14°C (57°F) three times a week for six weeks and concluded that this boosted the immune system "to a slight extent". It's also invigorating because it improves the circulation.

9 **KEEP THE HUMIDITY** in your house between 30 and 50 per cent so that the mucous membranes in your nose stay hydrated.

10 **BE OPTIMISTIC** (see page 91). Several clinical studies have shown a link between optimism and cell-mediated immunity. Suzanne Segerstrom and her team at the University of Kentucky followed 124 law students throughout one academic year and made them complete five questionnaires during this period. To test their immunity, candida yeast or dead mumps were injected under the skin of the forearm. The study found that the immune response rose and fell in line with their optimism.

IMPROVE YOUR Eyesight

Most people don't give a second thought to caring for their eyes; we take then for granted, and regularly place them under a lot of strain. Here are four easy exercises that will improve and protect your eyesight, and some diet and lifestyle suggestions.

NEAR–FAR VISION EXERCISE

This exercise helps to treat nearpoint stress, which is the leading cause of myopia (blurred distance vision). It is caused by spending too much time focusing on something close, like a book or a computer screen. It is important to take regular breaks from this kind of activity, and to allow your eyes to focus on something in the distance, otherwise over time the ciliary muscle inside your eyeball becomes too tight and unable to fully relax , so the crystalline lens of the eye gets locked into a fatter, thicker shape causing distant objects to remain blurred.

Hold your index finger about six inches in front of your face and focus on it for two seconds, then switch your focus to something that is at least twenty feet away, and hold for another two seconds. Continue to alternate your focus like this at least thirty times, so that you can feel your eyes being given a good workout.

PRESS GENTLY

Apply light pressure to your closed upper eyelids with the three fingers of each hand and hold for five seconds. Repeat eight times. This improves blood flow and gently stimulates the eye muscles.

MIDDAY REST AND RELAXATION

Give your eyes a rest during the middle of the day by closing them and gently cupping your palms over them to block out the light. Breathe slowly and deeply and gaze gently into the deepening blackness for at least five minutes.

IMPROVE BLOOD CIRCULATION

Close your eyes and keep them tightly shut for five seconds, then open them wide for five seconds. Repeat ten times, then spend thirty seconds blinking rapidly to clean and lubricate the eyes. This strengthens the muscles that control the eyelid, and improves circulation.

Changes to your diet and lifestyle will improve and protect your eyesight:

DIET

1. *Avoid sugary foods and refined carbohydrates which increase the risk of age-related macular degeneration (AMD).*
2. *Drink bilberry extract which contains the antioxidants Lutein and Zeaxanthin, also found in eggs.*
3. *Increase your intake of omega-3 fatty acid, which is found in oily fish and flax seeds.*
4. *Make sure you are getting sufficient quantities of vitamin C, vitamin E, beta carotene and zinc.*

LIFESTYLE

1. *Take a brisk thirty-minute walk at least four times a week. Exercise reduces the interocular pressure associated with glaucoma, and may reduce your risk of contracting it.*
2. *Turn down the heating in your house. If the ambient air gets too dry it will dry out your eyes.*
3. *Protect your eyes from bright sunlight by wearing sunglasses with strong UV protection to reduce risk of cataracts.*
4. *If you smoke, the most important way to protect your eyes is to quit. Smokers have a fifty per cent higher risk of cataracts, glaucoma, dry eyes and AMD than the general population.*

Most people accept that our thoughts affect our feelings and behaviour. We are encouraged to think positive thoughts because ruminating on negative thoughts is bad for us. However, did you know that the brain has evolved a systemic negativity bias? Rick Hanson, author of *The Neuroscience of Happiness,* explains: "to help us survive it preferentially looks for, reacts to, stores, and then recalls negative information over positive information". In other words, "the brain is like Velcro for negative experiences but Teflon for positive experiences".

Hanson shows how the negativity bias in our brains works. Neutral or positive moments "get remembered with standard memory systems, which is to say they're mostly in-and-out" but negative emotions "get stored in what's called 'implicit memory' – not so much memory for events, like what I did on my summer vacation, but rather the feeling of being alive. And that implicit memory bank gets shaded in a darker and darker way by the slowly accumulating residue of negative experiences."

Research by John Gottman, of the University of Washington, backs this up. He has shown that it takes at least five positive interactions to make up for just one negative one. This means that you have to make a special effort to reinforce positive experiences when they happen, and Hanson's book shows you how. He uses a three-stage method to reinforce positive events when they occur, with a powerful optional fourth extension stage:

1. *Turn a positive event into a positive experience by really focusing on it, actively bringing it forward in conscious awareness rather than letting it slip by.*
2. *Really savour it and make it intensely felt in the body. "Relish it, enjoy it, for 10, 20, or 30 seconds, so it really starts developing neural structure."*
3. *Make it your direct intention to take this positive experience and root it deep inside you so that it becomes part of you. In other words, "it's becoming woven into the fabric of your brain and yourself".*
4. *In the optional fourth step you can use the positive experience to help to heal a painful (but non-traumatic) memory. Take the painful memory and allow it to run "in the background of your awareness while the current positive experience that is its antidote is prominent and strong in a foreground of awareness, and hold both those things in mind for 10 or 20 or 30 seconds straight".*

THE TWO DARTS OF SUFFERING

Hanson introduces the Buddhist concept of the two darts of suffering. The first darts are the bad events and vicissitudes of life that everyone has to face – ageing, disease, death, pain. We compound our suffering with our own self-inflicted second dart, where we take a negative event and blow it out of proportion and let it hurt us even more. This means that when something negative happens it is vital to "automatically start activating the parasympathetic wing of the nervous system" by calming yourself down, taking deep breaths and being positive, so that you can minimize the negative bias.

WORKING MEMORY

"At present, working memory capacity is the best predictor for intelligence that has yet been derived from theories and research on human cognition."

Heinz-Martin Süß

Working memory (aka short-term memory) is the most important of all cognitive functions and it is a better predictor of school achievement than IQ. It is our mental notepad – the bigger the pad the more information you can process, understand and manipulate. It can also be compared to the control tower of a busy airport, scheduling and coordinating incoming and outgoing flights.

A task like remembering a phone number long enough to find a pen and paper to write it down relies on short-term memory, as does reading, because you have to be able to store and remember several words in a sentence long enough to work out the ideas that are being conveyed. If you are reading complicated material, you may have to keep several sentences and concepts in your short-term memory for up to a minute in order to follow an argument or line of reasoning. Improving your short-term memory improves all your cognitive abilities.

JONI HOLMES

Cognitive developmental psychologist Joni Holmes researches the role of working memory in learning and developmental disorders. In 2009 she published a study involving a group of school children identified as having working memory deficits who were given a computer-based training programme for 35 minutes a day. Tasks included hearing a series of letters and numbers and repeating them back, remembering the sequence of a row of lights and watching lights appear on a grid and then remembering the sequence after the grid had been rotated by 90 degrees. Over six weeks the tasks became progressively more difficult. The results were so dramatic that most of the children were no longer classified as having poor working memory and these benefits were still apparent when they were retested six months later. The children's IQ scores had not increased, but their learning ability had.

How to improve your working memory:

1 READ A BOOK

Whether for pleasure or digging into some demanding literature, reading is a great way to develop working memory. Challenge yourself with your reading material to experience the greatest improvement.

2 DUAL N-BACK

The free open-source version of the Dual N-Back exercise available at *http://brainworkshop.sourceforge.net* involves remembering the position of a blue square on a grid and the sound of a letter that accompanies it. In April 2008 a peer-reviewed scientific study showed that spending 20 minutes a day 4–5 days a week on this exercise improves working memory and fluid intelligence.

3 MEMORY SEQUENCING GAMES

These games sharpen your ability to remember the order of events, e.g. "I went to market and bought" where players take it in turns to add to the shopping list and remember what came before. Or try the electronic Simon game, where you have to remember a sequence of coloured lights (you can play an online version here *http://www.freegames.ws/games/kidsgames/simon/simon.htm* or google "Simon flash game").

4 FIRST-PERSON SHOOTER VIDEO GAMES

An increasing body of research shows that playing action computer games like Call of Duty improves working memory. A player has to keep a mental map of the location of other players as well as their playing styles and weaponry, hazards and rewards such as claymore mines and care packages. It requires rapid processing of sensory information and prompt action, and it is very motivating, encouraging the player to keep playing.

5 PLAY CONCENTRATION

A pack of matching pairs of cards are placed face down on the table; players take turns to flip them over two at a time and keep the cards if they uncover a matching pair, otherwise the cards are turned over again and play passes to the next person. The winner is the player who collects the most pairs.

6 LOOK, SNAP, CONNECT

This method was devised by Gary Small, a professor of psychiatry and ageing at UCLA. "Look stands for focusing attention. The biggest reason that people don't remember things is they're simply not paying attention; snap is a reminder to create a mental snapshot of information you want to recall later . . . and then the third step, connect, is just a way of linking up those mental snapshots, so an example would be if I'm running out quickly and I have two errands, pick up eggs and go to the post office. I might visualize in my mind and an egg with a stamp on it."

Sharpen your Awareness

OF THE HERE AND NOW

Most of us are always getting ready to live but never actually living. We either regret the past or hark back to a time when things were better, or else we worry about the future or fantasize about a better one. How many times have you ruined what should have been a pleasant experience by worrying about when it will end, or wishing you had done it sooner, or thinking of ways it could be better?

You can only play the ball in front of you. If you were playing a game of tennis you would naturally focus on the ball that is in play; it would be ludicrous to think about the point you just lost or how the next point will play out, and yet we do this with our lives all the time.

Living in the moment, or mindfulness, is intentional attention on the present. It doesn't mean having a blank mind or no emotions, but it does allow you the space to observe your thoughts and feelings without letting them control you. When you are mindful your focus shifts away from yourself and you become more connected to other people and the world around you.

Everyone agrees that living in the here and now is a good thing, but few people commit their entire focus to the present, even though it doesn't require years of training or meditation. All it takes is for you to decide to do it and to trust that it will bring positive results. You don't know what those results will be and you shouldn't grasp after them, because that would be living for the future, so just allow yourself the luxury of being where you are, doing what you are doing.

HABITS

Many bad habits (see page 98) are linked to a lack of mindfulness. We overindulge – shovel junk food in our mouths, smoke cigarettes or abuse alcohol without thinking, tasting or really savouring the experience in the moment.

BREATHE

When you are regretting the past or worrying about the future, spend some time focusing on your breathing. Take a deep breath in through your nose and exhale slowly through your mouth. And repeat for two minutes. Try it – it works. The simple act of breathing in and out will calm you down and bring you back to the present. Don't zone out though – allow thoughts to flow in and out of your mind and observe them with detachment. You can't change the past or the future by worrying.

FLOW

One of the best ways to live in the moment is to lose track of time – to set yourself a clearly defined and achievable goal and then become totally absorbed in the task. You can't force flow, you can only set up the conditions that will allow flow to occur – eliminate external distractions, clear your mind of the urgency of all other tasks and trust in your ability. Slow down, you're doing fine.

ACCEPTANCE (NOT RESIGNATION)

Some people argue that all human progress has been achieved by those who refused to accept their lot, and while this is true, if you allow your dissatisfaction and emotional pain to overwhelm you, you won't achieve anything. We all have pain and regrets, but we can only move beyond them by acknowledging their existence and accepting the emotions associated with them. Acceptance is acknowledging in a very real sense that you can't change the past and that the past need not affect your present experience. It is also accepting the moment rather that thinking of ways to improve it.

IMPROVE YOUR LONG-TERM Memory

BOMBARD YOUR SENSES

CHEWINGUM SUGAR FREE
IMPROVES THE MEMORY

Long-term memory is the continual storage of information for days, weeks and years, in contrast to short-term memory, which lasts for seconds or minutes. It also has an emotional component, since we often remember incidents from our past which affected us emotionally. Here are five ways to boost your long-term memory.

1 CHEW GUM

Dr Andrew Scholey, Professor of Behavioral and Brain Sciences at Swinburne University in Melbourne, Australia has done a lot of research into the effects of chewing gum on memory and mood. In a 2002 study he gave 75 adults a 20-minute test of memory and attention. Twenty-five of them were chewing gum, twenty-five mimicked the act of chewing, and the rest did not chew. The gum-chewers performed 24 per cent higher than the controls on immediate word recall tests and 36 per cent higher on tests of delayed word recall.

Scholey offers three potential explanations for this result. Two years earlier Japanese scientists had shown that chewing increases neural activity in the hippocampus, which is important for memory. Chewing gum causes the release of insulin, and insulin receptors in the hippocampus are also linked to memory. It also increases heart rate, increasing blood flow to the brain to improve memory.

A fourth factor may also be relevant: Scholey's recent research found that "chewing gum helped relieve anxiety, improve alertness and reduce stress among individuals in a laboratory setting". Stress reduction also improves cognitive function.

2 GET A GOOD NIGHT'S SLEEP

Studying for an exam just before you go to bed has been a well-known study tip for many years, but Dr Jozsef Csicsvari and his group at the MRC Anatomical Neuropharmacology Unit, University of Oxford have found evidence that it is more than an old wives' tale. Sleep is vital for the storage of new information and memory processing, so new information learned just before bedtime is reactivated in the brain during sleep.

Csicsvari's team observed the activity of pairs of neurons in the hippocampus of rats as they explored a new environment, and also while they slept. They found that the neurons that fired most frequently during waking exploration fired with corresponding frequency during sleep, indicating this consolidation process at work.

3 INVOLVE MANY SENSES

The best way to commit something to long-term memory is to bombard all your senses with relevant input so that many cross-references are created in the brain, enabling more reliable recall. For example, reading out loud targets hearing and sight simultaneously; you remember information better when experience is presented as an auditory-visual pair, much like in a real-life situation. By comparison, sitting at a desk reading silently to yourself is a less natural way to receive sensory input. Try to relate the information to smells, colours, sounds and tastes.

4 TEACH WHAT YOU HAVE LEARNED TO SOMEONE ELSE

This is one of the best ways to consolidate memory because it forces you to confront areas which are less well remembered or understood.

5 RECALL MULTIPLE TIMES

The more times you recall something the more firmly it beds into your long-term memory, so if you are learning for an exam, test yourself on the information after an hour, then again three hours later, and again six hours later, and then a final time before you go to bed.

IMPROVE YOUR Reaction Time

Reaction time is an important factor in many areas from sports and playing video games to real-life situations like driving a car. It is the interval between the arrival of a stimulus and your muscular response to it...

Several factors influence your reaction time, including your state of mind, relaxation, anticipation (being able to predict probable outcomes – for example a goalkeeper saving a penalty reads the body language of the kicker), the number of possible responses (the fewer choices the less time it takes to pick) and motivation.

WARM UP

Before you begin any activity that requires fast reactions make sure you warm up thoroughly. This activates your nervous system, warms your muscles, increases adrenaline and reduces the risk of injury.

RELAXATION

Reaction times are slowed by body tension, which can be caused by fear and anxiety. If you can control your anxiety and stay relaxed your body becomes more responsive and can achieve maximum speed and efficiency. People who are tense or inexperienced try too hard and rely on brute force; relaxation and experience allow more mental space to make better choices.

MOTIVATION

The more you want something, the higher your adrenaline levels, the more psyched you will be and the better your performance, subject to controlling your anxiety, which can also rise as motivation increases.

OVERSPEED TRAINING

This involves moving the whole body, or parts of the body, at speeds higher than the normal competitive speed. It trains you to think and act quickly and recruits more fast-twitch muscle fibres so that when you perform the activity at the normal speed it feels much easier.

ANALYSE YOUR RANGE OF CHOICES

Hick's Law states that reaction time increases in proportion to the number of possible responses, until a point where the response time is constant regardless – a curve which levels out into a straight line. You will benefit in any endeavour by analysing and filtering your range of choices for a given situation in advance, so that you can decide the best course of action instinctively in the moment. This is more than just having a game plan. High achievers are able to make split-second decisions with confidence because they have already spent many hours analysing and visualizing hundreds of different scenarios.

NO-MINDEDNESS

Martial arts rely on a fast reaction and observing subtle movements to anticipate whether an opponent is about to attack or defend. Bruce Lee stressed the importance of an attitude of emptiness which he called "Wu-Shin" or "no-mindedness", free from internal dialogue and trusting the unconscious mind to work exclusively for us when we trust it completely. Wu-Shin also embraces the idea of not grasping. Lee said, "Like everyone else, you want to learn the way to win, but never to accept the way to lose. To accept defeat – to learn to die – is to be liberated from it. Once you accept, you are free to flow and harmonize. Fluidity is the way to an empty mind. So when tomorrow comes, you must free your ambitious mind and learn the art of dying."

Aim to achieve a state of awareness that is open, non-emotional and not grasping after success, but living in the moment. For most people their performance suffers when they get angry or frustrated, leading to further failure. Successful athletes have a highly developed ability to control their emotions, so that they can maintain an emotionally neutral state of mind that is fully present.

IMPROVE YOUR MEMORY WITH Acupressure

Acupressure is an ancient Chinese healing method that involves applying firm pressure with the fingers to meridians and vital acupoints in the body; this improves circulation and encourages the flow of Chi, the life giving energy that unites body, mind and spirit.

The human body has fourteen meridians, twelve of which are associated with organs and functions of the body, and several hundred acupoints; an understanding of these underpins the whole of Chinese medicine, but you can still benefit from acupressure without having an in-depth knowledge of this complex system. All you need to start you off is to follow a few basic principles:

Apply firm pressure for two or three minutes using your thumbs, fingers, palm, side of the hand or knuckles. The pressure should be firm enough so that it hurts a little without becoming acute. If you experience severe pain decrease the pressure until you find a balance that is bearable. If you have medical problems, consult your doctor before trying acupressure and don't persist through agonizing pain. The pain should be a pleasing sign that your body is responding to change, not making you sicker. You may feel a little bit light-headed after treatment, but this will soon subside and be replaced by a feeling of energy and relaxation.

Sometimes you will feel stimulation (pain, an itch, etc) in one part of the body as you apply acupressure somewhere else. This referred pain is normal, and indicates that those areas of the body are connected.

After treatment drink two glasses of warm water. This helps flush toxins released by acupressure out of your body.

Six acupressure points to improve memory:

1 ONE HUNDRED MEETING POINT

Place your right hand behind your right ear and your left behind your left ear, then move your fingers up in a straight line until they meet on top of your head. You should be able to locate a small depression here. Press firmly on this point for at least one full minute.

2 THE DEPRESSION OF THE TEMPLES

Follow a line horizontally from your eyebrow until your fingers are resting in the depression of your temples. Press both points at once and hold for at east one minute.

3 THIRD EYE

This is located between the eyebrows just above the bridge of the nose.

4 THE GATES OF CONSCIOUSNESS

These points are two inches out from the middle of your neck, either side of your spine underneath the base of the skull.

5 THREE MILE

These two points are four finger widths below the kneecaps and one finger width outside of the shinbone.

6 BIGGER RUSHING

On top of your foot, between the bones where the big toe and second toe meet.

THE POWER OF Random INPUT

Random input is a technique for linking other thinking patterns into the ones we are already using. Everyone knows that emptying the mind through quiet contemplation gives your ideas breathing space, but the opposite strategy can be just as effective. Instead of depriving the brain of input, flood it with random influences and ideas, a rich soup of disparate data which you can combine to solve a problem by generating unique associations and new perspectives.

ASSOCIATION BOX

When you're boxed in reach for your association box. It's simply a container in which you collect lots of interesting clippings, photos, ideas, quotes, jottings, cartoons, doodles, advertisements – anything that stimulates ideas. Pick two or more items at random and associate them with your problem by pretending they are part of the solution and all you have to do is find the links. Your subconscious mind likes to make connections between things, because that's how it makes sense of the world. When the input is random, the results are often highly creative.

STUMBLEUPON

StumbleUpon integrates peer-to-peer and social networking principles with one-click blogging to create an emergent content referral system, helping you discover and share great websites. So whenever you press the Stumble button (which you can add to your browsing toolbar) you'll get a random page, or something geared towards your own user-set preferences. Tap into the power of the collaborative community to feed your thoughts: users recommend sites, which means you get to see stuff you wouldn't necessarily stumble upon on your own. See *www.stumbleupon.com*

THE DIRECTORS BUREAU SPECIAL PROJECTS IDEA GENERATOR

Creativity arises from the brain. Its essence is the ability to perceive and think in original and novel ways, and make original associations. TDBSpecialProjects Idea Generator is a three-wheel tool that strings together three words at random from its database: two adjectives followed by a noun. It may not appear very sophisticated, but if you leave your mind open to suggestion as you use the generator, you'll be surprised at the results this diverse input can bring. You can download as a widget to your mobile phone so you can generate ideas on the go. See *www.tdbspecialprojects.com*

PERSONAL ROSHI, THE NEURODYNAMIC ACTIVATOR®

During the last few decades there has been a lot of research into Alpha training instruments which can alter your brain waves. The most famous and controversial is the Personal ROSHI (pRoshi) created by Chuck Davis. A computer is used to monitor the moment to moment activity of a user's brain. That unique brainwave info is "fed back" to the person using special goggles that flicker coloured or multicoloured light. It uses random stimulation of the optic nerve to emulate the brain's own internal communication, to fool the brain into thinking it is receiving a message. Davis says its reaction is to generate brain waves similar to those of a Zen monk. The pRoshi can be yours for a mere $1,950.00. See *www.roshi.com*

Have you ever wondered why some people are wealthy while others are not? Have you ever noticed that wealthy people aren't always the most educated, the hardest working, or even the smartest? That's because millionaires attract the success they desire by breaking the bonds of limited thinking. Changing your mind will make you rich if you follow these eight rules:

1 SUCCESSFUL PEOPLE DON'T BELIEVE IN RANDOM LUCK

If you want more luck, take more chances, be more active, show up more often and connect with more people.

2 MILLIONAIRES DON'T BLAME OR ENVY OTHERS;

they take responsibility for their successes and failures, and they learn from them. Blame and envy leave you exhausted and inactive, which blocks wealth from entering your life.

3 CONFRONT YOUR BELIEFS ABOUT WEALTH – AND YOUR FEARS

For example, if you believe that money is evil or hard to get, you will have a hard time acquiring it. Your potential is determined or limited by your self-belief. Don't be afraid to fail. You only fail by not trying. What would you attempt if failure wasn't a threat?

4 FORM A CLEAR VISION,

backed by definite plans and a sustained unwavering belief. This will give you a tremendous feeling of confidence and focus, leading to success.

5 DO WHAT YOU LOVE AND THE MONEY WILL FOLLOW

Despite being worth US$62 billion, investor and philanthropist Warren Buffet says he isn't motivated by money, and has given most of his fortune to the Bill & Melinda Gates Foundation. He lives in the same house in the central Dundee neighbourhood of Omaha, Nebraska that he bought in 1958 for $31,500, and until recently drove a modest Lincoln Town Car. He spends at least 12 hours a week playing bridge (often with Bill Gates and Paul Allen). Do you spend 12 hours a week enjoying one of your hobbies?

6 FOLLOW YOUR OWN PATH

To become really successful, find your own voice and make your own path. You can copy someone's actions but you cannot successfully copy his or her goals or path in life.

7 CONSIDER THE PARET PRINCIPLE:

80 per cent of your income comes from 20 per cent of the work done. Concentrate more on effective tasks and less on auxiliary ones that don't bring in money directly (like preparation, cleaning, etc).

8 LEARN THE DIFFERENCE BETWEEN AN ASSET AND A LIABILITY

An asset is something that makes you money and a liability is something that costs you money. Reduce your liabilities and increase your assets. Poor people spend their money on prestige items (liabilities) to make other people think that they are wealthy; rich people buy or create assets which make them money. Only then do they buy the prestige items and they still have the assets.

Create a millionaire mindset by following the instructions above. Before long, miracles will start to happen in your life and blessings of wealth and abundance will start flowing in.

SPATIAL INTELLIGENCE

People with a highly developed visual perception of their environment who can manipulate three-dimensional images and shapes in their mind, solve puzzles likes a Rubik's cube or a maze and navigate well have good spatial intelligence.

Men have superior spatial abilities for some tasks and women have superior spatial abilities for others. Men are better at visual-spatial tasks (e.g. mental rotation) and spatio-temporal tasks (e.g. tracking a moving object through space) than women, but this has an environmental rather than a genetic cause. Women are better at detecting a hidden object than men. Evidence does not support men having better map reading skills.

Some studies have shown that women respond better than men to spatial-awareness training, and can perform as well as men after training. Men are better than women at video games such as Call of Duty, but that's because more men play the game than women. Stanford University School of Medicine research published in the

Journal of Psychiatric Research in 2008 showed that the reward centres of the brain were stimulated more in men than women during video-game play. Males are three times more likely to get addicted to video games than females.

So the good news is that spatial awareness is determined not by your sex but by your environment and motivation; there are lots of ways you can develop it:

Play chess, tic-tac-toe, draughts, Boggle, and any games which require you to manipulate a visual landscape.

Do mazes, jigsaw puzzles, tangrams (an ancient Chinese puzzle, consisting of seven geometrical pieces that form thousands of designs) and any puzzles that require you to perceive or process visual stimuli, forms or patterns. One of the earliest examples of this is Archimedes' Loculus, a puzzle consisting of 14 polygonal shapes that fit together in 536 distinct solutions to make a square or can be rearranged to make pictures of people, animals and objects.

Take up photography, painting, drawing, pottery, sculpture, flower arranging or graphic design.

Go orienteering or volunteer to be the navigator on a car journey.

Play with construction toys like bricks, Lego, D-Stix or K'Nex.

Get 3D CAD modelling software for your PC and start designing.

Play computer games.

Perform mental tasks that involve visualizing how parts can be assembled to form wholes (a typical right-hemispheric brain activity).

Google "Spinning Silhouette Optical Illusion" or "rotating dancer illusion". You'll see the silhouette of a rotating female dancer. Your brain decides whether she is rotating clockwise or anti-clockwise, and you can train yourself to change your perception of the direction by holding your index finger at eye level and pointing sharply to the left or right.

Learn an ideographic language like Chinese.

BINAURAL Beats

Binaural beats were discovered in 1839 by Prussian physicist and meteorologist, Heinrich Wilhelm Dove. They became popular in the late twentieth century as a way to induce well-being, relaxation, creativity and even arcane mental states like lucid dreaming and astral travel.

Using binaural beats is one form of "brainwave entrainment" in which external stimuli change brainwave frequencies to achieve a desired state of mind – alertness, concentration, relaxation, drowsiness or meditation. It is based on the principle that the brain responds to auditory (and visual) input by mimicking its wave frequencies. Brainwave entrainment has been used for centuries – most cultures use music and especially drum beats to create altered states of consciousness from shamanistic ritual to an Ibiza rave.

HOW THEY WORK

Binaural beats result from listening to two sounds – one in each ear – which differ slightly in frequency; the brain wave response and the resulting binaural beat depends on this difference. For example, if you play a sound with a frequency of 220Hz in one ear and 210Hz in the other ear, the brain hears the difference between the two (10Hz) as a deep pulse, which will induce an Alpha wave in the brain because its frequency is between 8 and 13Hz. If the two sounds had a frequency of 220Hz and 205Hz, the difference would be 15Hz, which would create a binaural beat in the Beta range (13–39Hz). Our ears can only hear sounds between 20 and 20,000Hz but a binaural beat is created inside the brain, which perceives it as a low-frequency beating tone. Some sources claim the difference between the frequencies must be less than 30Hz for the effect to be perceived, suggesting that binaural beats in the Gamma range are imperceptible though still beneficial.

Frequency range	Wave	Associated with
40–100 Hz	Gamma	High-level information processing, compassion, happiness, natural antidepressant
13–39 Hz	Beta	Left hemisphere, anxiousness, active concentration, quick thinking
8–13 Hz	Alpha	Right hemisphere, relaxation, creativity, suggestibility, balanced mood, drowsiness
4–8 Hz	Theta	Right hemisphere, subconscious mind, dream sleep, REM (Rapld-Eye Movement) sleep
0–4 Hz	Delta	Deep sleep, unconscious mind, intuition, psychic ability

HOW TO LISTEN TO BINAURAL BEATS

There are lots of binaural beats freely available on the internet, or if you prefer to part with cash, there are plenty for sale as CDs as well as MP3s. Some are just the pure sound waves, others are hidden within more melodious music. You can also purchase sets of tuning forks (sometimes advertised as expensive "Planetary Tuners") of varying frequency that will generate the same effect.

You must listen to binaural music with headphones, so each ear receives a different frequency. Make sure you choose the correct binaural beat to suit the appropriate wave frequency – you don't want to listen to Delta beats before an exam or Gamma beats to induce sleep.

Spend ten minutes every week reflecting on the positive things in your life for which you are thankful. You don't need to believe in a higher power to do this, nor does it mean that you are settling for things that need changing. Practising gratitude is a short time-out period which allows you to reprogram your brain to focus on what's going well.

It's easy to get so caught up with trying to make our lives better that we forget to appreciate what we have. By all means focus on material things but start with people and your valued relationships. This isn't a novel concept and it won't be the first time you've been advised to count your blessings, but it is included here because several scientific studies have shown that it works. In 2002 McCullough, Emmons and Tsang found a correlation between gratitude and happiness. Subjects were asked to write down five things for which they were grateful once a week for ten weeks. At the end of the study they were found to be twenty-five per cent happier than the control group.

Research by Sonja Lyubomirsky of the University of California, Riverside has found that "unhappy individuals construe experiences in ways that seem to reinforce unhappiness" while "truly happy individuals construe life events and daily situations in ways that seem to maintain their happiness". Gratitude is one of the mechanisms to achieve this. Lyubomirsky found that those who practised gratitude once a week were happier than those who did it three times a week. So when it comes to gratitude, less is more.

THE BENEFITS OF GRATITUDE

1. *It turns problems into challenges. If you are finding work tough, then be thankful that you have a job. If they don't pay you enough . . . at least they're paying you and looking for another job is much easier when you are employed. If work is boring be grateful that at least some of the people you work with are good fun. If work doesn't challenge you, be thankful that you are intelligent enough to demand more out of life than a dull repetitive job.*
2. *It reminds you what is important in your life. Wake-up calls like a divorce, a new baby or losing your job can be turned into opportunities for growth, so long as you recognize the power of your biggest resource – you.*
3. *It connects you to others and makes you more aware of your interrelationships and how you must reach out to them to offer help and receive it in return. Be thankful for all those connections.*
4. *It reminds you what others have done for you in the past and are doing now.*
5. *It makes you more generous. A 2010 study by David DeSteno and Monica Bartlett found that gratitude is correlated with economic generosity.*

HAPPINESS & SADNESS ARE LEARNED

Bad things happen to good people – wars, death, murder, theft, poverty – all of which make them unhappy. This chapter doesn't claim that you can transform these kinds of negative and traumatic experiences into happy ones (although looking for the positive outcomes can help to mitigate the pain). It is more concerned with the day-to-day experience of people in the West, with their busy lives and myriad worries and how they can teach themselves to be happier.

It is easy to be happy when the sun is shining, literally and metaphorically, just as it is easy to laugh when you experience something funny - these are the peaks that naturally arise from time to time. But with daily practise it is possible to raise your baseline happiness and put yourself in situations that promote happiness.

The highest baseline happiness has been found by doing FMRI (functional magnetic resonance imaging) scans of the brains of Buddhist monks. Studies have shown that the thickness of the cortex, the outer layer of the brain, on people who practise insight meditation which focuses on mindfulness was greater than the brains of non-meditators. The insula was thicker, as well as regions associated with attention and sensory processing.

Neuroscientist Sara Lazar explains, *"the insula is like a switchboard, connecting brain regions involved in emotions with those involved in thoughts and decisions. We believe this may contribute to stress reduction - thicker cortex probably means that this area is better able to coordinate these regions, thereby helping to resolve difficult emotional problems".*

SMALL CONCRETE STEPS

Happiness doesn't happen overnight: according to happiness expert, Gretchen Rubin, "it's possible to be happier by taking small, concrete steps in your daily life". She spent a year "test-driving the wisdom of the ages, the current scientific studies, and the lessons from popular culture about how to be happy - from Aristotle to Martin Seligman to Thoreau to Oprah". Her research (and subsequent best-selling book *The Happiness Project*) convinced her that you can train yourself to be happy.

TEN WAYS TO BE HAPPIER

1 *Make your number one priority close friendships with other people.* True friendship leads to a joyful life.

2 *Focus on your goals* rather than your fears, on what you want to accomplish, not what you are trying to avoid.

3 *Expect the best possible outcome,* and you will be more motivated to try to achieve it.

4 *Don't beat yourself* up if the outcome isn't everything you imagined.

5 *Appreciate what you have achieved* during a day rather than what went wrong or what you still have left to do.

6 *Set ambitious goals* and develop a profound sense of mission.

7 *Keep a happiness diary.* Each time something makes you feel happy or laugh, write it down. It makes you more mindful of the times when you are happy, and gives you something to cheer you up when you need a boost.

8 *Try to make other people happy.* This doesn't mean being a doormat people-pleaser, but happy people are socially-oriented and find happiness by helping others. One of the best ways to make other people happy is to be happy yourself.

9 *Remember* how little most things matter in the long run.

10 *Be persistent* and learn to enjoy the process rather than the results. Don't try to modify the entire world to fit in with your taste – that's impossible; change your mind instead. If you change your mind you change the world that you experience.

INCREASE Empathy

Empathy is the path to happiness because it helps us to connect with other people, to understand their motivations, and it teaches us about ourselves. It is a curious balance between seeing the similarities between yourself and others while at the same time resisting the urge to assume that they think like you...

If you are happy in your own skin it is much easier to see other people's viewpoints, without becoming judgemental or defensive, but if you are unhappy empathy is a good way to restore your mood. Most unhappiness comes from emotions that are directed towards other people, such as envy, anger and lust, but empathy enables you to take people off a pedestal or raise them out of the gutter.

GET IN TOUCH WITH YOUR OWN EMOTIONS AND INTERNAL DRIVES

Some people argue that great actors have empathy because they don't like themselves or don't know who they are, so they find relief by becoming someone else, and that therefore insecurity can be just as powerful a motivation to connect with others and find empathy than being secure. This is true, but it is harder to be empathetic when you hate yourself than if you accept yourself and your flaws.

RECOGNIZE AND ACCEPT YOUR OWN WEAKNESSES

This needn't stop you from trying to change them and you'll find it easier to forgive other people theirs. The biggest step you can take towards empathy is to recognize that everyone has insecurities, everyone is trying their best to muddle through life and deal with the human condition; some people hide their insecurities by being nasty or super-confident, and some are undoubtedly born with more opportunities than others, but the grass usually isn't greener. That's why empathy is the perfect antidote to envy and is a path to happiness. If you are envious of someone, take a good look at their entire life, don't cherry picks the good bits that you covet for yourself.

TRAVEL

This broadens the mind and is a great way to increase your empathy, so long as you don't compensate for the culture shock by developing an ex-pat mentality and entrenched belief in the superiority of your homeland.

LISTEN

Empathy rarely involves a great deal of talking. Even telling someone "I know how you feel" isn't always the most appropriate response (as any recently bereaved person knows). When powerful emotions are being conveyed, effective listening takes a lot of courage; it can make the listener feel vulnerable and powerless , which is why so many of us make the mistake of offering solutions or try to change the other person's mind (often to cheer them up) rather than validate their feelings and accept that their interpretation of facts and events is true to them, even if they are negative.

We all have a strong urge to feel understood. Empathy is easy when two people share the same viewpoint, so by definition when the greatest need for empathy arises, there will be an inherent conflict, requiring you to park your own urge for validation so that you can put yourself in the other person's shoes.

PAUSE

Allow yourself time and mental space to assimilate what the other person is feeling. Don't jump in with solutions or rebuttals, even if you are trying to help them. Sometimes empathy simply needs silence. This allows you to collect your thoughts and remain emotionally available.

GROW MORE Brain Cells

In 1928 Professor Santiago Ramon Y Cajal published an article called "Degeneration and Regeneration in the Nervous System" in which he stated: "in adult centres the nerve paths are something fixed, ended, immutable. Everything may die, nothing may be regenerated." This idea remained unchallenged for seventy years until a 1998 report in the journal *Nature Medicine* showed that although the vast majority of brain cells are created in the womb, neurogenesis – the growth of new brain cells – takes place all the time, especially in areas such as the hippocampus.

"What the researchers discovered was that within each of our brains there exists a population of neural stem cells which are continually replenished and can differentiate into brain neurons. Simply stated, we are all experiencing brain stem cell therapy every moment of our lives," says neurologist David Perlmutter, author of *Power Up Your Brain*.

We have stem cells in our brains that develop into neurons and the process is regulated by our DNA. A single gene – the BDNF gene – codes for production of a protein called brain-derived neurotrophic factor (BDNF) which supports the survival of existing neurons and the growth of new neurons and synapses.

Perlmutter recommends four ways to encourage the growth of new brain cells: "The gene that turns on BDNF is activated by a variety of factors including physical exercise . . . curcumin and the omega-3 fat, DHA."

1. PHYSICAL EXERCISE

In addition to the many well-documented benefits of exercise, studies with laboratory rats have shown a link between exercise and levels of BDNF. Studies of humans with Alzheimer's disease have found that regular exercise shows improvements in cognitive functions, including memory, language and attention, of up to 1,800 per cent.

2. CURCUMIN

Curcumin, the main active ingredient in the spice turmeric, increases BDNF. Scientists believe this is one of the reasons that rates of Alzheimer's disease in India, where turmeric is widely used, are one quarter of those in the US.

3. DOCOSAHEXAENOIC ACID (DHA)

DHA is an omega-3 fatty acid found in high concentrations in algae and fish oils. A recent trial led by Dr Karin Yurko-Mauro involving 485 healthy people with memory complaints with an average age of 70 years, found that those "who took algal DHA capsules for six months had almost double the reduction in errors on a test that measures learning and memory performance versus those who took a placebo . . . The benefit is roughly equivalent to having the learning and memory skills of someone three years younger." In Japan DHA is used to enrich some foods and students routinely pop DHA pills before exams.

DEVELOP YOUR Intuition

Intuition can be a peculiar bag of tricks and so much new-age nonsense surrounds it that many people have come to associate intuition with psychic abilities, tapping into the universe and allowing yourself to be guided by something bigger than yourself. That's all very well if you believe in it, but developing your intuition can actually be a very practical and simple process of stripping away rather than layering on esoteric theories about the cosmos. You can increase your intuitive capacity with simple daily practice.

Intuition involves bringing data and input from the subconscious into your conscious awareness so that you use it to help you make more complete choices. For example, common sense should tell you that it is a bad idea to park your car in a poorly lit, run-down car park in a bad area of town, but rationality doesn't always provide the whole picture. The car park might be brightly lit, and yet still you get a gut feeling that something is wrong. Maybe your subconscious has registered something lurking in the shadows, or you saw a report on the TV about a spate of car thefts from this very car park, but haven't consciously made the connection. In this case, listen to your intuition and move your car. What's the worst that can happen? You spend an extra five minutes parking.

If you function with purity of intent then you are less focused on yourself and more likely to trust your intuition. Many of us have been trained to ignore our emotions and to base our decisions on hard facts, but, especially where people are concerned, you have to cultivate empathy (see page 75) and become sensitive to non-verbal cues, because social interaction is multi-layered and complex. Also our ego and impatience can get in the way and make us ignore gut signals.

BE ATTENTIVE AND OBSERVANT

The more open you are to your surroundings and to the subtext of what people are saying to you, the more intuitive you will become. People with excellent powers of observation can astound others with their apparent intuition, when actually they are very skilled at watching and listening.

KEEP A DIARY TO RECORD YOUR INTUITIVE IMPRESSIONS

This will help you to spot meaningful coincidences (synchronicity), keep track of how effective your intuition is and have fun making new and interesting connections. Creating and noticing patterns is a powerful human instinct and can help to bring some order to a world that sometimes appears disconcertingly chaotic.

HOW TO HAVE MORE Eureka! MOMENTS

Dr David Rock, founder of the NeuroLeadership Institute and CEO of Results Coaching Systems, a global consulting firm, teaches that we should allow the unconscious mind to solve complex problems rather than gnaw away at them with our conscious logical mind.

He has asked thousands of people how they solve complex problems and they gave similar answers, that the insights "always suddenly arrive, either as you fall asleep, in the middle of the night, as you wake up, as you exercise, shower or drive. Or while doing something pleasant and repetitive, like knitting, gardening or cooking." By following a few simple rules he claims we can "dramatically increase the likelihood that an insight emerges".

1

The first requirement is quiet. Rock says, "insights tend to involve connections between small numbers of neurons . . . [they] require a quiet mind, because they themselves are quiet". He quotes neuroscientist Mark Jung-Beeman to support this: " . . . variables that improve the ability to detect weak [neural] associations may improve insight solving". We can only detect these weak associations if we reduce the background activity in our brains that is drowning them out.

2 *"Insights are more likely when you can look inside yourself and not focus on the outside world." The mind is most likely to reach an insight when it is wandering, like a form of daydreaming.*

3 *Research by Mark Jung-Beeman proves that "Participants higher in positive mood solved more problems, and specifically more with insight, compared with participants lower in positive mood."*

4 *Having an insight is "not effortful . . . if you want insights you need to stop trying to solve a problem . . . Also, effort tends to involve a lot of electrical activity, and can reduce the likelihood of noticing the quiet signals of insight. The point is, you have to let go of the problem for the solution to come to you."*

The next time you need to solve a complex problem, don't make yourself a cup of coffee, surround yourself with data and furrow your brow with intense concentration. This generates the wrong sort of brain activity and increases anxiety. Instead, go and perform a task that is quiet, easy, repetitive, and allows the mind to wander cheerfully. If you are brainstorming in a group, build in some quiet, individual reflection time.

If the solution still doesn't pop into your head, don't despair. That evening remind yourself of the problem before you go to bed and your subconscious will continue playing with possible solutions while you sleep. The comedian John Cleese is keenly aware of the power of the subconscious mind. When he gets stuck writing a sketch at night he goes to bed and the following morning "not only [is] the solution to this problem immediately apparent to me but I [can't] even remember what the problem had been the previous night". He describes an occasion when he lost a script, rewrote it from memory and then discovered that the second version was better. His explanation: "after I had finished writing the original the unconscious part of my mind must have continued working on it . . . so I began to see that there was . . . a part of my mind that was helping me to be more creative".

MORE EFFECTIVE Listening

Effective listening is the single most important verbal skill you can possess; without it effective communication is impossible. Many people are under the mistaken belief that they are good listeners while making a host of errors that telegraph that the conversation is about them rather than the other person; these include focusing on what you will say next, interrupting, dividing your attention, offering solutions when none are sought, and failure to understand what is really being said – the subtext. The golden rule with listening is to do to others as you would want them to do to you. Here are ten ways to become a more effective listener.

1. DON'T INTERRUPT

This may seem simple but we all interrupt and often think we are making a positive contribution; shut up and pay attention to what the other person is saying. You can only understand and learn when you stop talking. Always make a point of keeping quiet until they have finished; you'll soon notice how many times the urge rises in you to interrupt – these are places where you would have interrupted or lost focus if you hadn't been making a conscious effort to keep quiet. The only exception is asking questions (see below).

2. LET THEM TALK MORE THAN YOU

From now on whenever you have a conversation try to notice who does the most talking, and always aim to make it the other person. Sales people are trained to do this because they know that when the other person is talking they are telling you what they want and you are learning important information. All the sales person has to do next is to fulfil this want. This is even more true during an argument – if no one feels they are being listened to the argument escalates.

3. HAVE ATTENTIVE BODY LANGUAGE

If you're a poor listener your body language will give you away. Make sure you face the speaker directly (all too often we conduct awkward conversations while standing at right angles to one another, and then wonder why we feel so unnatural). Maintain eye contact (but don't overdo it – keep it natural and comfortable). If you are sitting, sit straight and lean forward slightly. Nod occasionally, smile and use other facial expressions. Don't fidget or try to perform another task; stop what you are doing, turn off the TV, eliminate all other environmental distractions and just listen.

4. ASK QUESTIONS AND/OR REFLECT

Asking questions or reflecting on what the speaker has said are great ways to show that you are engaged and to keep the conversation moving forward and to clarify what is being said. You also learn more. Ask one question at a time and wait for the answer rather than cram three into one sentence.

5. RESPECT THE SPEAKER

The best way to make people respect and listen to you is to be a good listener. You won't impress anyone if you spend the whole time they are speaking planning your witty and intelligent reply/riposte. Show them respect first by listening, without judgement.

6. KEEP AN OPEN MIND

Don't judge, second-guess or make assumptions about what the speaker is saying, otherwise you will misinterpret. Keep an open mind; you may not agree with them but this should not prevent you from listening without prejudice. Sometimes we are so wrapped up in our own version of what we think the other person is saying or is about to say that we miss their point completely. Grow antennae, not horns. Keep your mind still as well, so it isn't racing with your own ideas or distractions like what you're going to buy for dinner this evening.

7. IMPROVE CONVERSATIONAL SKILLS

Good listening (not clever talking) improves your conversational skills the most. It enables you to move the conversation forward, plus you retain more information, so the next time you speak you can break the ice by asking something relevant that relates back to the last time you spoke; the person will be impressed that you remembered, and this will make them feel that you care about them.

8. FOCUS ON THE SPEAKER, NOT YOURSELF

The next time you feel self-conscious during a social interaction there's a good chance it's because you're focusing too much on yourself rather than listening. It is impossible to be self-conscious if you are truly directing all your focus on another person.

9. LOOK FOR THE SUBTEXT

Don't take everything at face value; try to be sensitive to and acknowledge the others person's feelings and what they are really trying to say. You may value straight talking and have little patience for anything else, but the reality is that people obfuscate for all sorts of reasons, out of politeness, fear, emotional distress or insecurity. Hearing the subtext gives you a better chance to put them at their ease and communicate candidly and authentically.

10. WORK HARD AT ACTIVE LISTENING

It takes a lot of focused concentration, self-awareness and even humility, but it is the best way to show and command affection and respect.

AUGMENT Sleep

We all know the importance of getting a good night's sleep – it improves our mood, aids concentration, boosts the immune system and allows the brain to sort out what it has experienced during the day, committing useful data into the long-term memory. Feeling tired all the time is unpleasant, but did you know that lack of sleep is linked to obesity, heart problems and depression?

Few of us make sleep a priority, but it is just as important as healthy diet and exercise. One in three people have sleep problems and most just don't get enough of it. Here are eight ways to encourage deep, restorative sleep.

1 AVOID STIMULANTS AND DEPRESSANTS

Avoid eating and drinking anything that interferes with sleep at least four hours before bedtime. This includes caffeine, alcohol, cigarettes, a large meal and fizzy drinks. A hot milky drink aids sleep because it contains calcium which helps relaxation and tryptophan which your body uses to make the hormone serotonin. Use skimmed milk, because fat will stimulate digestive activity and keep you awake. Eat a light meal several hours before bedtime and cut out the late night snacks.

2 HAVE A BATH

There are two theories about why this aids sleep. In his book *Counting Sheep*, Paul Martin advises taking a warm bath one to two hours before bedtime, because the drop in body temperature when you get out of the bath signals to your body that it is time to sleep. The second approach calls for a very hot bath, which relaxes your muscles and leaves you feeling dozy. Do whatever works best for you.

3 GO TO BED AT THE SAME TIME EVERY NIGHT

Your internal body clock or circadian rhythm is controlled by the hypothalamus, a part of the brain the size of an almond which also controls body temperature, hunger and thirst. If your bedtime varies by several hours, your body clock becomes confused and you experience mini jet lag.

4 MAKE YOUR BEDROOM A SLEEP-FRIENDLY ZONE

A bedroom should be quiet, dark, cool (around 65° F or 18° C), well-ventilated and should only be used for sleep and sex. Don't work in bed or watch TV, and keep computers in another room. If you live in a noisy neighbourhood, this will disrupt your sleep even if it doesn't keep you awake; white noise (an un-tuned radio) is a good way to block out environmental noises.

5 EXERCISE EARLY

If you exercise in the evening, make sure it is at least three hours before you sleep, otherwise the cortisol in your bloodstream will keep you awake even if your muscles are tired.

6 SAY "THE"

Instead of counting sheep to block out unwanted thoughts, choose a single short neutral word like "the" and repeat it at irregular intervals to prevent your mind from running over the problems of the day.

7 WAKE UP AT THE SAME TIME EVERY MORNING

If you go to bed at the same time, your body should wake up naturally leaving you more refreshed than being woken against your will by an alarm clock. Too much sleep can be just as exhausting as too little, so only lie in if you have to catch up on missed sleep. If you need an alarm clock to wake you up, go to bed earlier.

8 BUY A NEW BED

If your bed is more than ten years old, buy a new mattress. Old beds have poor lumbar support, which affects your sleep and may damage your spine. If you wake up with a sore back or an aching neck, your mattress or pillow are probably to blame.

Rediscover YOUR OPTIMISM

When life keeps knocking you down it's hard to stay positive, when there doesn't appear to be anything coming your way that remotely resembles good luck. When everything feels like a hard slog being optimistic can feel Pollyanna-ish, but optimism is good for your health and makes you more available to spot opportunities when they do arrive.

Professor Richard Wiseman started his working life as an award-winning professional magician, then became a psychologist. He wrote *The Luck Factor* based on a ten-year research project into the psychology of luck. He says *"luck is not a magical ability or the result of random chance. Instead, although most people have almost no insight into the real causes of their good and bad luck, their thoughts and behaviour are responsible for much of their fortune".*

He devised an experiment which showed that "lucky people consistently encounter opportunities whereas unlucky people do not". He asked a group of test subjects to read through a newspaper and count the number of photographs, but on one of the pages he had placed a large message which said "Stop counting, tell the experimenter you have seen this and win £150". The people who considered themselves unlucky missed it, while the lucky ones tended to spot it. He concluded, "Lucky people are more relaxed and open, and therefore see what is there rather than just what they are looking for."

The same applies to optimism. If you believe in the best possible outcome you are more likely to achieve it. Make these simple changes in your behaviour and you will attract good fortune.

1 SMILE MORE OFTEN

It makes you feel happier and it lets other people know that you are approachable and friendly.

2 THINK THE BEST OF PEOPLE

This may mean that you occasionally give someone the benefit of the doubt when they don't deserve it, but at least you won't feel like the whole world is out to get you and you won't end up gossiping and bitching, which makes other people trust you less.

3 FACE FACTS

Optimism and realism are not mutually exclusive. Pessimism and negativity often make us remain passive, fearful and in self-denial.

4 CONFIDENCE HELPS

Approaching problems and challenges with the confidence that you will find a way through actually helps you to face up to your responsibilities.

5 AVOID NEGATIVE INFLUENCES

Don't associate with pessimistic people who make you feel bad or who encourage harmful behaviour. Surround yourself with positive, successful people and it will rub off on you. Also limit your exposure to negative news stories.

6 SEPARATE THE PAST FROM THE FUTURE

Animals learn to avoid danger by remembering what happened in the past. However, just because you've had bad experiences in the past doesn't mean that you must repeat them in the future. Everybody faces situations that are out of their control, but they don't last forever.

7 LEARN TO ACCEPT THE THINGS YOU CAN'T CHANGE AND CHANGE THE THINGS YOU CAN

See yourself as a creator rather than the victim of circumstance. You can make things happen rather than let them happen to you. Take responsibility, but don't blame yourself if things don't always work out as you planned – failure and disappointment are part of life.

8 CULTIVATE HUMILITY

The less you focus on yourself the less likely you are to fall into the negative self-centred belief that the universe is against you. You are just like everyone else, trying to do the best for yourself and your loved ones.

Ear MASSAGE

Massage your ears daily and your whole body will benefit, especially your brain. This simple act triggers the release of endorphins, reduces anxiety and tension in the jaw and neck, stimulates the immune system, increases blood flow and aids relaxation.

Our ears contain lots of energy points that connect to your whole body. The Chinese have used ear reflexology – acupressure and acupuncture – for thousands of years to boost brain power and improve well-being.

Here are five therapeutic ear massages that have a deeply nourishing effect on the nervous system. Within minutes they will make you feel more energized and help you think more clearly...

1 DYNAMIC MASSAGE

For a full energizing ear workout, pinch both ears between your index and middle finger at the jaw line and press gently as you rotate in small circles anticlockwise five times. Then apply gentle pressure to the indention underneath the ear. As the blood flows, your ears may start to tingle or itch; follow the impulse and rub or flick them rapidly to satisfy the urge. Then starting at the bottom of the ear, press with your index fingers as you move up and behind the ear. Keep massaging for as long as feels comfortable, or until the itching subsides. Notice the heat, and increase in energy and blood flow. You should now feel more energized and alert.

2 UNROLL YOUR EARS

Before you start a new task, improve concentration by gently unrolling the rim of your upper ear, all the way round, stroking/squeezing between index finger and thumb. Repeat three times.

3 EAR LOBE

Gently massage your ear lobes in tiny circles as you pinch them between thumb and index finger. After a few minutes move your attention to the middle of the outside of your ears, and gently rotate your entire ear in circles.

Massaging the right ear lobe stimulates the left brain and pituitary gland (responsible for lots of body processes including growth, blood pressure, temperature regulation and sexual function). Massaging the left ear lobe stimulates the right brain and pineal gland (which controls wake/sleep patterns. René Descartes called it the "seat of the soul" and the point of connection between the intellect and the body).

4 AURAL WARMTH

Rub your palms together vigorously to generate heat, then cup your palms over your ears. Hold for about 30 seconds and repeat five times.

5 PULL YOUR EAR LOBES SEVEN TIMES

Take your earlobes between your thumb and forefinger and lightly pull downwards. Breathe out gently. Repeat seven times. You should feel freshness in your eyes and your hearing will become clearer.

Speed Reading

"I took a speed reading course and read *War and Peace* in twenty minutes. It involves Russia."

Woody Allen

As children we are taught letters, then words and sentences, but many people still make the effort to read word by word even in adulthood. Efficient reading and speed reading means letting go of childish reading habits and looking for clues to meaning rather than taking in every individual word. Speed reading is a trade-off between speed and comprehension but no matter how fast you read your comprehension shouldn't suffer and in many cases it will improve.

1 *Eliminate distractions.* You may be able to read despite background noise, and you may even believe that playing music helps you to concentrate but the best condition for reading is silence, because anything that takes up your brain space is a disturbance. Sit in a comfortable chair, in a room with a comfortable temperature and adequate lighting.

2 *Understand the function and context of your reading and what information you want to gain from it.* Looking for specific facts is very different motivation to understanding key concepts of a philosophical argument or reading a novel for pleasure. Before you read the body text, skim the introduction, contents, first and last paragraph of each chapter and sleeve notes to contextualize the material quickly. This will give you a framework on which to build the rest of your comprehension.

3 *Reading isn't linear;* the eye doesn't travel smoothly across the page, it skips back and forth, stops and starts, varies in speed. To speed read you need to set a faster pace and read smoothly, minimizing skip backs, picking out the key words that carry the meaning.

4 *Use your peripheral vision.* The fastest readers can take in large blocks of text in one go; some readers move their eyes down the middle of the page and pick up the key text on either side peripherally. This is less tiring for the eyes and makes less demands on your short-term memory.

5 *Make a conscious effort to avoid skipping back to re-read.* Often this is a sign that your attention has begun to wander. If you are skipping back a lot, take a five-minute break. To help you to keep a fast and consistent pace run your finger along the line (this is called the Wood Method, devised in the 1950s by school-teacher and speed-reading pioneer Evelyn Wood).

6 *Don't mouth the words or speak them in your head (sub-vocalize).* Just allow the blocks of meaning to pass into your consciousness. Hearing the words slows you down.

7 *You don't need to read every word.* In fact aoccdrnig to rscheearch at Cmabrigde Uinervtisy, it deosn't mttaer in waht oredr the ltteers in a wrod are, the olny iprmoatnt tihng is taht the frist and lsat ltteer be at the rghit pclae.

REPLACE BAD HABITS *WITH* GOOD ONES

Aristotle said that "we are what we repeatedly do". Most of us are defined and controlled by our habits. Just one or two bad habits can hold you back considerably – financially, emotionally, in career and in health.

If you've ever taken a walk in hilly sheep country you'll notice that sheep walk along well-worn pathways. Why should they use another route when this one is the path of least resistance? It's the same with a bad habit. Unless you establish a new more positive route you'll just keep on trudging along the old one.

ACKNOWLEDGE THE NEED FOR CHANGE

Breaking a habit is hard. The first step is recognizing the need to change, which must come from you, and not from someone else telling you to stop. This can only happen when you acknowledge the damage it is doing. This takes courage, but it also requires a strategy. Most people fail because they don't follow this simple rule: the best way to quit an old habit is to replace it with good ones.

FIND A NEW HABIT

If you quit something without finding positive replacements you soon feel deprived. If you want to quit smoking , take up chewing gum; instead of a glass of wine have a cup of stone-ground Japanese green tea – it will feel like an indulgence but it will cost you less than the wine and will be better for your health.

EXERCISE

Exercise is a great replacement for a bad habit because the endorphins produced make you feel good; if you take up an exercise class, you can get the social interaction that you might be seeking by an expensive Friday night spent clubbing.

GIVE YOURSELF REWARDS

The short-term reward the bad habit gives us is more tempting than the long-term reward of not doing it. Human beings like rewards so they motivate us. Unfortunately when a reward does more harm than good we call it a bad habit and try to quit, but we often neglect to reward ourselves for positive behaviour.

Research proves that behaviours are reinforced when they are followed by a reward. If you save £200 a month by quitting smoking, use £50 each month to buy yourself a treat. This should be guilt-free because you're only spending a quarter of what you used to spend on smoking. A reward also helps you to focus on something positive. For example, if you are dieting, then allowing yourself a single cream cake once a week should be seen as a reward rather than a relapse which destroys your motivation. The problem with habits is that they often make us feel guilty because they give us unearned rewards; in turn this guilt can make us seek the comfort of the bad habit, creating a vicious circle.

ONE HABIT AT A TIME

Focus on making one big change and stick to it for thirty days, rather than kick five habits at the same time. Also give yourself simple rules to follow.

FIND YOUR TRIGGERS

Bad habits come with triggers. For example, you might get the urge to smoke after a meal, when you read the paper in the morning, or as you drive to work. Spend a few weeks writing down your triggers as they occur – every time you get the urge, write down what caused it. Then you've got more chance of avoiding these situations or recognizing a pattern, making it easier to resist.

REPLACE LOST NEEDS

Your good habit must provide some or all of the benefits that the bad habit gave you. If you want to cut down on going to the pub, then find another activity that gives you social interaction and excitement. Everyone is different, but you might find that playing competitive sport, or taking a class gives you the same buzz and is better for your health and finances, makes you more likely to stick with it.

REPLACE LOST

ESTABLISH A PREDICTABLE ROUTINE

Your good habit schedule should require the minimum of thought and broker no negotiation. If you've resolved to exercise for thirty minutes every day, plan the week ahead when this will happen and stick to it, otherwise you will make excuses. So, Tuesday evening is your Step class, Thursday lunchtime you always walk the dog for four miles. Create a routine that you don't have to think about and can't talk yourself out of on a whim. The more your good habits can become automatic, the more satisfied and in control you will feel.

CREATE A GOOD HABIT CHAIN

Get a big year planner wall calendar and put a big green cross or a sticky gold star (adults can have gold stars too!) on it for every day that you feel you have stuck to your new positive habit, then simply try to maintain the chain. As the days go by you'll see your progress building and you'll have a strong incentive to keep up the good work. You can also mark reward days on your calendar to use as mini goals. Don't beat yourself up if you have a lapse, but see building a chain as a way to promote and visibly record positive behaviour. This will remind you how much you have achieved, rather than what you are giving up, plus the odd lapsed days will seem less significant.

TAKE ONE DAY AT A TIME

The only way to control the future is to focus on the present. Don't think about what you are giving up forever, just focus on making today count.

NEEDS

TAKE A Power Nap

"Take off your clothes and get into bed. That's what I always do. Don't think you will be doing less work because you sleep during the day. That's a foolish notion held by people who have no imaginations. You will be able to accomplish more. You get two days in one – well, at least one and a half."

Winston Churchill

The power nap has been with us for decades, but it's always worth revisiting an old friend. Power napping is no substitute for a full night's sleep which is necessary for many vital body functions, but studies have shown that it improves mental performance, balances hormone levels and reverses information overload. Don't feel guilty for power napping; it isn't lazy and you'll be in good company – high achievers like Leonardo da Vinci, Napoleon and Churchill all took a daily early afternoon snooze.

The National Institute of Industrial Health in Japan has found that in workers who took a 15-minute nap after lunch "perceived alertness was significantly higher in the afternoon after the nap than after no nap". Harvard researchers have also shown that a midday nap reduces the risk of heart problems by 34 per cent.

There are four stages of sleep and they were first described as long ago as 1937 by Alfred Lee Loomis using electroencephalography. The stages relate to the brain wave activity. Stages N1 and N2 are light sleep, N3 is deep sleep and the final stage is REM sleep, associated with dreaming. The term "power nap" has been attributed to Cornell University social psychologist James Maas (author of *Power Sleep*) who points out that naps "greatly strengthen the ability to pay close attention to details and to make critical decisions".

The most important thing to remember when having a power nap is to restrict it to no more than twenty minutes, so you don't enter Stage N3. Entering deep sleep without completing the sleep cycle results in sleep inertia, drowsiness and headache rather than a feeling of refreshment. Take your short power nap just after lunch because your circadian rhythms make a late afternoon doze more likely to turn into deep sleep leaving you feeling worse than before. Maas advises that "naps taken about eight hours after you wake have been proved to do much more for you than if you added those 20 minutes onto already adequate nocturnal sleep".

CAFFEINE NAP

It is important to take regular breaks when you are driving and a caffeine nap is your best option. Professor Jim Horne and Dr Louise Reyner of Loughborough University performed a driving simulator experiment to see which of these eight alternatives gave the most benefit: cold air, radio, a break, a nap, caffeine pill, placebo, caffeine pill and a nap, placebo pill and a nap – caffeine and a nap came out top. If you drink a cup of coffee and nap for twenty minutes the coffee won't disturb your sleep because its alerting affect will take about half an hour to act.

DEVELOP FOCUS & Concentration

If you find it hard to concentrate it doesn't mean that you are lazy; you simply need to do some mental organizing to help you to eliminate distractions. All successful people in the world bar none have highly developed powers of focus and concentration, which go hand in hand with knowing what they want, setting clear short- and long-term goals, working on one thing at a time and being willing to put in an extra ten per cent of effort along the way...

From sporting excellence to great works of art, nothing worthwhile was ever created without focused concentration. If you want to improve your powers of concentration follow these four principles:

1 SET GOALS AND PRIORITIES

It is very difficult to apply yourself to any task if you don't know why you're doing it. Before you begin, decide what you want to achieve and why. Also, work out what's in it for you and for other people. Does it further your long-term goals, and if it doesn't, is it a distraction, or is it something you could postpone, or delegate to someone else to do (even if it means paying them)?

2 PRIORITIZE

Complete your daily tasks in order of priority, and focus on one thing at a time. If you can't complete a task immediately (for example, you're waiting for a phone call or a delivery), move onto the next task and wipe the previous one from your mind while you work. If it is a chore like vacuuming that just has to be done, then set a time limit and give yourself a reward afterwards. Give all your attention to the task in hand, rather than worry about all the other things you've left to do.

3 CONCENTRATION DEFEATS FEAR

One of the greatest distractions is fear – usually fear of the consequences if we fail to complete the task, or if we do it badly. If you apply all your attention to the task in hand, there is no mental space for fear.

4 FOCUS MEANS SAYING NO

Having focus means saying no, not just to distractions, but more importantly to choices which do not take you where you want to go. For example, Steve Jobs, CEO of Apple says, "Apple is a $30 billion company, yet we've got less than 30 major products . . . we tend to focus much more. People think focus means saying yes to the thing you've got to focus on. But that's not what it means at all. It means saying no to the hundred other good ideas that there are. You have to pick carefully."

CROSSING THE Midline

This is your vertical midline, and being able to cross it – reach your left hand over to the right side of your body to pick up a ball, for example – is a vital development skill and a prerequisite for whole-body coordination and cognitive development in babies and young children.The right side of the brain controls the left side of the body and the left side of the brain controls the right side of the body. Some children have a problems crossing the midline, so instead of reaching over to one side to pick up an object, they will switch hands at the midline rather than cross back.

Even though you mastered this skill before you could crawl (an excellent crossing the midline activity), you can still derive great benefit from spending a few minutes each day doing exercises to cross the midline.

CROSS CRAWL

Cross crawling is one of the best crossing the midline exercises and it has even been shown to improve literacy levels among illiterate prisoners. Make sure you alternately move one arm and its opposite leg followed by the other arm and its opposite leg.

LAZY EIGHTS

This is a key exercise in Brain Gym®, an educational, movement-based programme aimed at enabling children and adults to reach their potential. Draw a very large horizontal eight on the wall and then use your finger to trace repeatedly along the curves and watch your hand closely as you perform the movement. This promotes hand-eye coordination and creates a rhythm and flow. After twenty passes, repeat with the other hand.

TWO-HANDED DOODLING

Colour in a picture or doodle using a pen in each hand. Or you could write out a sentence, alternating each letter between right and left hands.

BOUNCE AND CROSS

Sit in a chair with your legs slightly apart. Hold a ball in your right hand, bounce it once on the floor and catch with your left hand, then pass your left hand across your midline and place the ball in your right hand; then return your left hand to the left side of your body and bounce the ball again, and so on. Try to establish an even rhythm to the count of four. For a demonstration of this exercise being performed see *http://www.youtube.com/watch?v=tnMkGvd3Qeo*

ELBOW TAP

Stand with your arms at your sides. Bend and touch your right elbow to your left knee as you raise your left leg, then return to starting position, then touch your left elbow to your right knee. Repeat gently and rhythmically twenty times.

TOUCH TOES

Stand with your legs wider than shoulder width apart. Bend at the waist and tap your right foot with your left hand, curl back up to standing and then touch your left foot with your right hand, and curl back upright. Repeat ten times.

Neurobics

GIVE YOUR BRAIN A NEUROBIC WORKOUT AND CHALLENGE YOUR GREY MATTER

It is widely accepted that increased mental alertness comes from using your brain in new ways. Neurobic exercises involve taking a sideways step away from routine to stimulate new neural pathways, with the added benefit that they do not require expensive equipment, a computer, or even a pen and paper...

Neurobics went mainstream during the 1980s when Dr Lawrence Katz and Manning Rubin coined the phrase to describe brain exercises that fulfil three criteria. A neurobic exercise must:

1. *engage one or more of your senses in a new way*
2. *involve your full attention*
3. *deviate from your normal routine*

Neurobic exercises are thought to delay brain ageing by encouraging the growth of dendrites inside the brain. These are the short branching fibres that grow from a neuron and increase the surface area available for sending and receiving information.

Mental decline is associated with shortening of dendrites, widening the synapses between cells so information is transmitted less efficiently, leading to memory loss and other cognitive impairment.

Take a simple routine task like brushing your teeth. You do it every day, probably without thinking, maybe when you're half asleep. However, simply holding the toothbrush in your other hand and giving it your full attention turns the task into a neurobic exercise. Throughout your day there are lots of opportunities to turn a routine task into a neurobic workout. Not only will it stimulate your brain, but it's also fun and encourages you to interact with your environment in a new way. The most refreshing immediate benefits of a neurobic exercise are that it brings you more fully into the present moment and makes you feel more alert and alive. Long term, the change of routine and perspective can have profound effects on how you conduct yourself and approach other challenges in your life.

FIVE WAYS TO GIVE YOUR BRAIN A NEUROBIC WORKOUT

Here are five ways to give your brain a neurobic workout, and you can devise your own so long as they meet the three criteria mentioned.

1. *Take a shower with your eyes closed. Your other senses will become more active. You will become more aware of the sound of the water as it cascades off your body and slaps onto the floor. The smell of the shampoo will be heightened, your whole body will become more responsive to the warm water. Your spatial awareness will be challenged as you grope for the soap and lunge for the sponge.*
2. *Take a new route to work or school.*
3. *Use your non-dominant hand to perform a routine task, like brushing your teeth, spreading jam on your toast, pouring a cup of coffee, writing or using your PC mouse.*
4. *Hold a conversation using gesture and sign language instead of talking.*
5. *Operate an elevator using only the Braille symbols.*

For more information about neurobics, read *Keep Your Brain Alive: 83 Neurobic Exercises to Help Prevent Memory Loss and Increase Mental Fitness* by Dr Lawrence Katz and Manning Rubin.

Zap Dyscalculia

If your mental arithmetic skills aren't up to scratch, you can draw some comfort from a recent electrifying discovery: neuroscientists at Oxford University have found that transcranial direct current stimulation (applying a tiny electrical current to the brain) improves people's mathematical abilities for up to six months.

Dr Roi Cohen Kadosh and his team used 15 student volunteers, aged 20–21. They were taught symbols that corresponded to different numerical values, and then made to perform a series of standard tests for assessing mathematical abilities using these symbols. Five volunteers were given either a placebo or a low electrical stimulus (one thousandth of an amp) running across the right parietal lobe – an area of the brain at the top of the head that is vital for mathematical processing (people with dyscalculia often have abnormal parietal lobe function).

Those who received the electrical current running from right to left performed well, while those who received the current from left to right performed with a level of skill equivalent to a six-year-old. The first group was tested six months later and still maintained a high level of performance.

The electrical stimulation was pain free; some subjects reported a mild tingling sensation in the affected area.

Reporting on his findings Kadosh warned:

"Electrical stimulation is unlikely to turn you into the next Einstein, but if we're lucky it might be able to help some people to cope better with maths . . . much more research is needed before we can even start thinking of this kind of electrical stimulation as a treatment".

However, he was still very positive about the results:

"We are extremely excited by the potential of our findings and are now looking into the underlying brain changes."

Dr Roy Hamilton, co-director of the Laboratory for Cognition and Neural Stimulation at the University of Pennsylvania is confident that maths isn't the only ability that can be enhanced by electricity. He says that if the device is used to stimulate a different part of the brain it could result in superior language abilities.

Zap

The most important thing about meditation is that you mustn't try to chase results. The only commitment you need to make is to promise yourself that for one week you will set aside a few minutes each day to experience this simple exercise. No one is judging you, nor should you judge yourself. Meditation is a time to observe your thoughts without judgement, or striving for results. Just deciding to start meditating and committing yourself for seven days are two results right there – not that you're counting, right?

Sit or lie somewhere quiet, warm and comfortable where you know you won't be disturbed. Spend a few moments getting comfortable and allow your focus to come gently towards your body as it slowly relaxes. Breathe normally – don't exaggerate your breathing, or become fixated on it. Just allow your body to relax a little more each time you exhale, and relax your abdomen so that your lungs and diaphragm can receive the next breath. Become aware of any areas of tension, but don't worry about them or try to do anything about it.

Keep breathing gently and if it helps you to relax, visualize each part of your body in turn sinking downwards, supported by the floor – start at your feet and work up to your head, and visualize the muscles, tendons and bones relaxing. If you feel like sighing as you exhale, follow the impulse, but keep things light and flexible – there's no need to get fixated on any method. Just follow whatever comes naturally to you to help you to relax your body.

Now that your body is more relaxed bring your attention towards your mind. Allow your thoughts to pass through your mind without trying to stop them. Just observe. Don't try to stop thinking, just become a spectator. Don't worry if your mind is racing, or if you don't feel relaxed enough – just be aware that you are judging yourself. Let that go. There is no failure, no right and wrong, just the process. Relax and see what happens.

Focusing on your breathing is a good way to calm the mind. Observe how you are breathing and take slower, deeper breaths, as low down into your abdomen as possible. Again, don't worry about whether you are doing it right. Observe that thought and let it go. Just stay present in the moment. If you notice your mind is wandering, gently bring your attention back to your breathing.

Whatever you are feeling is what you are feeling. There is no judgement, just you sitting or lying here, engaging in meditation for as long as you want. Don't try too hard. Enjoy the feeling of quiet relaxation.

What could be simpler than this meditation? It doesn't require any fancy theories, just daily commitment, regular practice, no judgement or grasping after results. Just you, present in the moment with your relaxing body and thoughts.

LOOK

NEUROECONOMICS CAN HELP MAKE YOU Rich

Neuroeconomics combines biology, psychology and economics to try to understand how markets behave and how people act when they try to make money. In *Your Money and Your Brain: How the New Science of Neuroeconomics Can Help Make You Rich*, Jason Zweig explores the reasons why investors make bad decisions, and repeat those mistakes over and over again, by examining what happens in our brains when we seek and gain reward. He has discovered several mechanisms which have evolved to encourage us to seek rewards and avoid danger, which can be a hindrance when it comes to investing.

Our brains seek food, sex, love and shelter (rewards), while avoiding danger from wild animals, other humans and the environment; consequently they seek reward and shun risk. Unfortunately when it comes to investing this often leads us astray. Zweig concludes that the market is intrinsically irrational because investors act more emotionally and less rationally than they realize.

ANTICIPATION AND REWARD

Zweig met up with Brian Knutson, a neuroscientist at Stanford University, who got him playing an investing video game while a functional magnetic resonance imaging (fMRU) scanner measured his brain activity. He found that winning did not give the brain as much pleasure and stimulation as the anticipation of winning did. The thrill of anticipation is the driving force that motivates human activity, putting the body on a state of high alert, acting as what Paul Slovic, a psychologist at the University of Oregon, calls a "beacon of incentive". Zweig says "this seeking system functions partly as a blessing and partly as a curse". He cites as an example the stock of Celera Genomic Group which dropped more than 20 per cent in the two days following the announcement that they had successfully completed sequencing the 3 billion molecular pairings of the human genome. "Celera had achieved a scientific miracle. So what happened? The likeliest explanation is simply that the anticipation of Celera's success was so intense that reality was a letdown."

LONG-TERM MEMORY

The other measurable effect of anticipation of reward shows up in the hippocampus, an area of the brain associated with long-term memory. The anticipation of reward is more important for forming memories than receiving the reward. However, while the brain responds more to the hope of big rewards than small ones, it is less sensitive to changes of probability of receiving a reward. This is what drives irrational greed and makes us gamble against poor odds when the rewards are high. The burst of anticipation that fires in the brain when faced with the chance of a large reward overrides the analytical areas of the brain. "Your expectation of scoring a big gain elbows aside your ability to evaluate how likely you are to earn it. That means your brain will tend to get you into trouble whenever you're confronted with an opportunity to buy an investment with a hot – but probably unsustainable – return." This explains why investors become overconfident when faced with bigger rewards.

FEAR AND DANGER

Zweig has also analysed the way our fear and memory interact and he observes that we often pay more attention to the least likely dangers, such as sharks, bears, snakes and alligators, when statistically, deer (running in front of vehicles) are responsible for seven times as many human deaths per year than the other four animals combined. This same fear makes us misjudge the market, and instead of assessing risk by looking at how frequently bad things have occurred in the past, we draw upon our most vivid and most recent memories, causing us to make bad decisions based on emotion rather than rational probability.

PEER PRESSURE AND THE HERD MENTALITY

Decisions made in isolation vary considerably from those made in a group. Zweig refers to an experiment conducted by Gregory Berns where people were asked to judge whether three-dimensional objects were similar or different. Subjects judged correctly 84 per cent of the time when they were on their own, but this figure fell to 59 per cent when they were part of a group of five "peers" who were actually colluding with the researcher. Brain scans showed that there was high activity in the amygdala – associated with fear and pain –

when subjects defied consensus, indicating that following the herd is attractive because it is less painful than social isolation. This same herd mentality leads to bubbles and crashes, while smart investors are able to stay rational, trust their judgement and take a more balanced long-term approach.

PATTERN SEEKING

"Humans have a phenomenal ability to detect and interpret simple patterns," says Zweig, but "when it comes to investing, our incorrigible search for patterns leads us to assume that order exists where it often doesn't." Our quest for consistent and repeatable trends causes us to make bad investments based on decisions that fly in the face of statistical probability. For example, if you flip a coin and get nine heads in a row, this pattern may either convince you that the next flip will also be heads, or that it can't possibly happen again, so you plump for tails. Of course, the probability of heads remains the same as it always was – 50/50.

So, is ignoring our emotions the route to investment riches? Not quite. Zweig concludes that successful investors like Warren Buffet do not ignore their emotions, "they turn them inside out" and use them to prompt further analysis. "When they feel fear, they don't act on it. They examine it. They say, what should this feeling tell me?" They remain rational and analytical in spite of their greed and fear.

The Power of Laughter

When was the last time you laughed – really laughed, laughed so hard and long that you felt a bit woozy afterwards, your eyes were streaming and your chest was aching with the effort? If you can't remember, then you need to think seriously about upping your laughter quotient.

Every day you should try to laugh like this; not only will it reduce stress, but it will increase your life expectancy, boost your immune system, improve your relationships and increase your baseline well-being.

THE BENEFITS

Laughter has been clinically proven to combat stress. When you laugh, endorphins are released into the bloodstream, your muscles relax, your blood pressure lowers, levels of cortisol decrease and a boost of extra oxygen is circulated around your body. Research at Loma Linda University School of Medicine has also shown that the amount of activated T lymphocytes, which play a central role in cell-mediated immunity, increases. So don't wait until you are stressed to get your daily dose of side-splitting laughter, make it part of your daily routine. Clearing ten minutes of quiet time in the morning to watch a sitcom or your favourite comedian will leave you feeling more prepared to face whatever comes your way. Even forcing a laugh is better than nothing, and if you persevere it may even turn into a self-induced hysterical laughter workout.

NORMAN COUSINS

The illness and recovery of the American author and political journalist Norman Cousins is a testament to the power of laughter. At the age of eleven he was misdiagnosed with tuberculosis and confined in a sanatorium; even then he "set out to discover exuberance". In later life this attitude helped him battle heart disease and the pain of arthritis. He developed his own recovery programme combining huge doses of Vitamin C and lots of Marx Brothers films. "I made the joyous discovery that ten minutes of genuine belly laughter had an anaesthetic effect and would give me at least two hours of pain-free sleep," he reported. "When the pain-killing effect of the laughter wore off, we would switch on the motion picture projector again and not infrequently, it would lead to another pain-free interval."

THE WORLD LAUGHTER TOUR

Laughing is even more fun when it's shared. Founded in July 1988 by psychologist and self-styled "joyologist" and "Cheerman of The Bored" Steve Wilson, The World Laughter Tour ("Think Globally, Laugh Locally") has a unique ethos summed up by the phrase "Don't Postpone Joy". After being inspired by several gurus in India who were teaching the importance of using laughter for physical and mental health, Wilson resolved to spread their message around the world. WLT now has a presence in many countries, with dedicated authorized representatives. See *http://www.worldlaughtertour.com* for details on how to set up a laughter club in your area.

Mood and happiness are linked but they aren't the same thing. Think of the former as the weather and the latter as the climate. Your overall levels of happiness may be heating up but that doesn't stop you from having days that are cold and gloomy. So, what you can do to lighten your mood is not necessarily the same as what you need to be happy. We're talking quick fixes rather than life changes, but since a life lived is a series of moments . . . you get the picture. Anyway, here are ten ways to lift you up and put you in a better place.

1 *Phone a friend, or better still, hang out with them.* Despite what you might think when you're feeling low, humans are social creatures and need company. Hooking up with a good friend is the best way to stop you dwelling on your own problems and inadequacies.

2 *Give yourself a treat*, something just for you and it doesn't have to be food or expensive. Pampering yourself with a hot bath (but not too hot), having a nail makeover or a hot stone massage is not only relaxing but it will send your subconscious the message that you value yourself and that you deserve to be treated well.

3 *Look at your holiday snaps.* According to researchers at the UK's Open University, looking at personal photos of a happy occasion is eleven times more effective at lifting your mood than listening to music, eating chocolate, drinking alcohol or watching TV. So break out your holiday snaps and wallow in some happier times.

4 *Go for a walk outside.* In addition to all the health benefits, walking outside exposes you to sunlight (it doesn't matter if it's cloudy). Studies have shown that people who get the most sunlight, especially in the morning, report better moods. To help you sleep better, limit your light exposure in the hours before bedtime. If you don't like walking, invite a friend along or borrow a dog for an hour. Studies by Professor Jules Pretty and colleagues at the University of Essex have found that as little as five minutes of moderate exercise outside has a significant effect on mood, so why not cut out a few cups of coffee and take a quick walk around the block instead.

5 *Light a scented candle* or diffuse a calming essential oil such as lavender, bergamot, jasmine, lemon balm, rosemary, vetiver or ylang ylang. Stimulating your olfactory system is a fast track to reducing anxiety and feeling more positive.

6 *Avoid drugs and alcohol.* They affect brain chemistry and just store up more problems.

7 *Drink a cup of milk thistle tea*, made by adding a few drops of high quality extract to near boiling water. The milk thistle is a flowering plant of the daisy family (Asteraceae). It has been used for centuries to protect the liver against toxins, but it is also a mood booster. Its key ingredient is a flavonoid called silymarin, and the only known source is the milk thistle seed.

8 *Write your feelings and worries down on paper.* Just getting them out of your head can be enough to stop them from playing on a repetitive loop, or stop half-formed worries eating away at your self-esteem. Then, put the list aside and spend twenty minutes doing something that requires your full concentration

9 *Take responsibility but don't blame yourself* – guilt and inadequacy be gone. This leaves you better placed to see the bigger picture and put your feelings in proper perspective.

10 *Don't be brave. Cry. It's good for you.* Tears help to remove toxins built up in the body from stress; they contain protein and beta-endorphin, one of the body's natural pain relievers. Dr Margaret Crepeau, professor of nursing at Marquette University, has studied tears in relation to wellness and has found that "well men and women cried more tears more often and at more times than did men and women with ulcers and colitis . . . Laughter and tears are two inherent natural medicines whereby we can reduce duress, let out negative feelings, and recharge. They truly are the body's own best resources."

Willpower IS NOT A LIMITED RESOURCE

Willpower is the ability to overcome laziness and procrastination and to persevere with a task until its successful accomplishment.

For years educators, self-help gurus and even scientists have argued that when willpower is at a low ebb, the only way to restore it is to take a break and recharge. We tend to think of it as a limited resource; some people have more than others but when the tank is empty, all you can do is take a break and let it fill up again. However, a recent study at Stanford University published in *Psychological Science* in 2010 has shown this to be wrong. It seems the urge to refresh is mental rather than biological.

Veronika Job, Carol Dweck and Greg Walton made participants perform standard concentration tests after they had already spent time doing other tiring and demanding tasks. Those who believed or were led to believe that willpower was finite performed worse on the tests than those who believed or were led to believe that willpower was infinite and within their control.

The scientists also found that leading up to final exam week the willpower-is-finite group procrastinated 35 per cent more and ate junk food 24 per cent more often than the other group.

Veronika Job says, “if you think of willpower as something that’s biologically limited, you’re more likely to be tired when you perform a difficult task. But if you think of willpower as something that is not easily depleted, you can go on and on.” Dweck adds, “Students who may already have trouble studying are being told that their powers of concentration are limited and they need to take frequent breaks. But a belief in willpower as a non-limited resource makes people stronger in their ability to work through challenges.”

Thought STOP

Thought stopping is a recognized cognitive restructuring technique taught by psychologists and other healthcare professionals...

It is so simple that at first it might seem like common sense, but it is a powerful way to stop ruminating thoughts from repeating in your head. Some people spend all day with a negative internal dialogue running in the back of their mind. Here's how to stop it:

Yell "Stop!" (or if you're in public, scrunch your eyes tight and yell it in your head).

If that sounds all too obvious, consider that when you do this something very powerful happens: you immediately become self-aware. In that moment you have recognized that the thoughts may be damaging, so it gives you the opportunity to confront them. When we are lost in thoughts and worries we have no self-awareness so these negative thoughts have complete power over us. Saying "Stop!" snaps you into the present so you can create a better outcome.

Troubling thoughts need to be addressed rather than ignored. Saying "Stop!" doesn't get you out of your responsibilities; it is designed to make you aware of irrational and destructive thoughts so that you can take action (if procrastination is the cause of your anxiety) or recognize that you are being irrational.

Suppose you arranged an important meeting for a week's time and the other person said that on no account must you cancel. You promise you won't let them down. Then two days later six inches of snowfall means that you can't get your car off your drive let alone make the 200-mile journey to the meeting. More snow is forecast for the next few days. You send an email suggesting that you postpone the meeting but because you don't get a reply you begin to ruminate that either they haven't received your message or that they are really angry with you. By the following day it enters your thoughts once every five minutes but you ignore it. Ignoring thoughts is not the same as saying "Stop!" Only then can you examine the issue and take action. You decide to phone to speak to them in person. They aren't angry; they agree with you and you reschedule the meeting. Saying "Stop!" was the kick-start of self-awareness you needed to move forward, rather than live with energy-sapping intrusive thoughts.

Thought stop is also a good way to beat a craving, or stop you from impulse buying something you could live without. If you are trying to lose weight, say "Stop!" the next time you get the urge to stuff something unhealthy into your mouth. Wait two minutes and the craving will pass.

tive

CAPABILITY

The romantic poet John Keats only mentioned his theory of "negative capability" once, but this significant idea lies at the heart of all creative accomplishments. In a letter to his brother dated Sunday, 21 December 1817, he says, "at once it struck me, what quality went to form a Man of Achievement especially in literature & which Shakespeare possessed so enormously – I mean Negative Capability, that is when man is capable of being in uncertainties, Mysteries, doubts without any irritable reaching after fact & reason".

Keats believed that great achievement and creativity was made possible by a willingness to accept that there are some things that cannot be explained by rational thought and logic, that there always remains a mystery that cannot be fully understood. In fact, as he stated in a letter to his friend Benjamin Bailey a month earlier: "I am the more zealous in this affair because I have never yet been able to perceive how anything can be known for truth by consecutive reasoning." He is talking about intuition and metaphysics, but also about the creative process itself.

THE SFUMATO PRINCIPLE

Michael Gelb, author of *How to Think Like Leonardo da Vinci*, has been inspired by the same principle, only he calls it The Sfumato Principle, which he says is essential for his creativity. Sfumato is an Italian word which means "going up in smoke" and it is the name of one of the four canonical painting modes of the Renaissance, involving subtle blending techniques and gradations of light and shade as used in Da Vinci's most famous painting, the Mona Lisa. Negative capability has also been compared to German philosopher Martin Heidegger's concept of Gelassenheit, "the spirit of disponibilité [availability] before What-Is which permits us simply to let things be in whatever may be their uncertainty and their mystery".

According to Dr David Rock, author of *Your Brain at Work: Strategies for Overcoming Distraction, Regaining Focus, and Working Smarter All Day Long*, "the brain is primed to experience at least a mild threat from most forms of uncertainty". Great artists, actors and musicians are able to tolerate and even enjoy the uncertainty of the creative process, rather than try to nail everything down to create a performance or piece of art that "works". It doesn't mean getting so lost in the process that you never achieve anything, rather that the longer you allow yourself to exist with the uncertainty the more chance you have of something really special and original happening.

ART & FEAR

The quest for control and assurance is detrimental to our creativity, as David Bayles and Ted Orland explain in their book *Art & Fear: Observations on the Perils (and Rewards) of Artmaking*: "People who need certainty in their lives are less likely to make art that is risky, subversive, complicated, iffy, suggestive or spontaneous. What's really needed is nothing more than a broad sense of what you are looking for, some strategy for how to find it, and an overriding willingness to embrace mistakes and surprises along the way . . . uncertainty is the essential, inevitable and all-pervasive companion to your desire to make art. And tolerance for uncertainty is the prerequisite for succeeding."

EMBRACE UNCERTAINTY

Expand your creativity, happiness and mental health by embracing uncertainty. Don't rush to solve a problem. See unpredictable situations as opportunities to explore not only your own abilities and talents, but to have new experiences. Frustration and depression are often the result of things not turning out the way we insist. Anxiety builds when we don't know how the future will turn out; many of us turn to unhealthy things like alcohol, food or smoking, to combat the anxiety caused by ambiguity. The publisher Robert I. Fitzhenry said, "Uncertainty and mystery are energies of life. Don't let them scare you unduly, for they keep boredom at bay and spark creativity."

CHALLENGE Assumptions

Challenging assumptions is one of the best ways to generate new ideas. All social reform and many inventions, scientific breakthroughs and leaps in human knowledge were made by people who were prepared to challenge their limiting beliefs and assumptions, and more importantly, those of their contemporaries.

Albert Einstein shook the foundations of physics with his theory of special relativity by having the courage and insight to challenge the Newtonian model of gravitation which had been unquestioned for more than two hundred years; Marie Curie, pioneer in radioactivity, the first European woman to earn a doctorate in the sciences and to receive a Nobel Prize, opened the doors of science to women worldwide by challenging gender assumptions; in the seventies Bill Gates stunned computer hobbyists by asserting that there could be a commercial market for computer software; Usain Bolt became the fastest man in the world by challenging the assumption that sprinters must be compact and muscular and that height is detrimental to explosive speed.

Interestingly, this is also the mechanism by which much comedy works – it sets up a premise that we fall in with because we make assumptions, then the pay-off reveals our assumptions to be false, which makes us laugh. Funny, isn't it, how sudden recognition of the error of our beliefs should make us laugh? Some would argue further that comedy exists precisely to challenge assumptions and to undo society's preconceptions and prejudices.

LATERAL THINKING EXERCISES

Here are three lateral thinking exercises. The solutions are simple but in each case a single assumption prevents most people from seeing them:

1. A man and his son are in a serious car crash. The father dies instantly, but the son is taken to A&E. Upon arrival the surgeon says, "I can't operate on this boy, he is my son!" How can this be?

The surgeon was his mother.

2. A woman gave birth to two sons on the same hour of the same day of the same year. But they were not twins. How can this be?

They were two of a set of triplets.

3. A man is wearing all black – black trousers, shirt, shoes, socks, coat, gloves. He is walking down a back street with no street lamps. A black car comes towards him with its headlights off but still manages to stop in time. How did the driver see the man?

It is daytime.

REVERSE ASSUMPTION

This technique involves reversing a problem to find a solution and has much in common with Reverse Brainstorming (see page 134). The oft-cited classic example of this is when the car maker Henry Ford took the prevailing assumption that success lay in finding a faster way to get the workers to the parts and reversed it. His solution which revolutionized manufacturing: finding a faster way to get the parts to the workers.

"IN ALL AFFAIRS IT'S A HEALTHY THING TO HANG A QUESTION MARK ON THE THINGS YOU HAVE LONG TAKEN FOR GRANTED."

BERTRAND RUSSELL

The next time you have to solve a problem in your life write down all your assumptions about it and examine them. Often your own self-imposed rules, preconceptions and assumptions prevent you from seeing the way forward.

It has often been said that genius is born not made, but actually there is a strong case to show that the opposite is true. Albert Einstein, one of the most famous geniuses who has ever lived, said "Everybody is a genius. But if you judge a fish by its ability to climb a tree, it will live its whole life believing that it is stupid."

Clearly genius relies on finding something for which you have a natural talent and interest, but what is the missing ingredient? Geoff Colvin, author of *Talent is Overrated: What Really Separates World-Class Performers from Everybody Else* argues that great achievers from Mozart to Tiger Woods were not born with a mysterious divine gift but developed their seemingly miraculous skills by hour upon hour of "deliberate practice". Furthermore, this practice isn't very enjoyable, so it takes a very motivated individual to do what is required, day after day, week after week, year after year. If we are willing to make this commitment "great performance is in our hands far more than most of us ever suspected". For those seeking excellence he views the hardness of deliberate practice as a good thing, because "it means that most people won't do it. So your willingness to do it will distinguish you all the more."

Colvin begins his thesis by asking the simple question: Why are there so few people who are world-class excellent at what they do? He says that "this is a mystery so commonplace that we scarcely notice it yet it's critically important to . . . success or failure". He observes that "most people are just okay at what they do" despite the many hours they may have dedicated to it. In fact, Colvin points out, "extensive research in a wide range of fields shows that many people not only fail to become outstandingly good at what they do . . . they frequently don't even get any better than they were when they started".

DELIBERATE PRACTICE

Deliberate practice is a large concept, and you should read Colvert's book for a thorough explanation. "Deliberate practice is hard. It hurts. But it works. More of it equals better performance. Tons of it equals great performance . . . For starters, it isn't what most of us do when we're practising."

It has five main elements:

1. *It is designed specifically to improve performance; this requires a teacher, coach or mentor, who can draw on decades of study into the field, provide a second perspective, help you devise a programme for improvement and give feedback on that practice.*
2. *It can be repeated over and over again "to a stultifying extent".*
3. *Feedback on results is continuously available. Practising without feedback will not generate improvement.*
4. *It is very demanding mentally, which is why four or five hours a day appears to be the upper limit of this sustained concentration. If it doesn't challenge you with intense, difficult effort, it probably isn't deliberate practice.*
5. *It isn't much fun, which is why the vast majority of people don't do it. Focusing on your weaknesses is painful and yields long-term rewards, which is why most of us prefer to practise what we can already do well, and then congratulate ourselves on a feel-good workout.*

FOR UNEXPECTED RESULTS

REVERSE BRAINSTORMING

FUN & EXCITING

If brainstorming feels a bit passé and doesn't seem to be solving your problem, try reverse brainstorming. It's more fun and can yield some unexpected results. It combines brainstorming with reversal techniques to help you generate even more creative ideas through cynicism, sarcasm and hostility. Anticipating potential failures is especially important when an idea is new, hard to put into practice or you have little margin for error.

Instead of asking "How can I fix this problem?" ask yourself, "How can I cause this problem?"; instead of considering "How do I achieve these results?" consider "How do I cause the opposite results?" Instead of "How can I succeed?" try "How can I really mess up?" Once you have brainstormed all possible solutions to the reversed problem, you can flip them into solutions to create the desired results. Imagine you were running a health club and you wanted to brainstorm how you could improve the customer experience. Try to solve the problem "How can I make the customer experience worse?"

Some of your answers might be:

Double book appointments; play loud rock music in the treatment rooms; betray customer privacy; have untrained instructors; install bright fluorescent strip lighting; make people feel rushed; make treatments as painful as possible; double prices; serve greasy junk food in the restaurant, etc.

Next, brainstorm how to reverse these ideas into potential solutions:

1. *Double book appointments: some customers might like group treatments with a friend. We should cater more for group bookings.*

2. *Play loud rock music in the treatment rooms: the traffic noise from the road outside can be intrusive. Let's soundproof the front windows and walls so serenity begins as soon as clients check in.*

3. *Have untrained instructors: we should make sure that the training certificates of our staff are framed and highly visible in the waiting room, and provide cash incentives to our staff to become more highly trained.*

4. *Make people feel rushed: after a session has finished we should give customers as much time as they need to get dressed and gather themselves. Make sure that we leave fifteen minutes between room bookings, so no one ever feels hurried.*

5. *Serve greasy junk food in the restaurant: only sell branded food that has a high degree of identification with the healthy values for which we stand.*

One of the most revealing things about reverse brainstorming is that it can highlight several areas where worst practices are already running rampant. Often we know what we should be doing right, but it can take a reverse brainstorming session to draw attention to our own laziness and self-deception.

Declutter

Chucking out your junk and tidying up what's left is one of those mind-changing tips that is so simple and ubiquitous that many people overlook it, even though they readily spend money and time looking for more esoteric solutions to their melancholy and mental muddiness. Even if you don't struggle with clutter, taking greater control of your immediate environment is a good path to better mental hygiene. Here are nine ways to make your home a cleaner, happier place.

William Morris said "Have nothing in your home that you do not know to be useful, or believe to be beautiful." Take a hard look at all the knick-knacks, trinkets and decorations in your house and apply that rule.

1. *Stop bringing stuff into the house,* or make it a rule that for every item you collect you have to get rid of two (the One-in-two-out-rule).

2. *Do one room at a time* otherwise you will get overwhelmed. Also having one nice room is a good incentive to keep it tidy and spread the good work to other rooms. Start at the corner by the door and work your way around the room. Whip round once doing superficial stuff like emptying bins and picking up litter, then go round again paying attention to the smaller details.

3. *Work in small bursts* – fifteen minutes each day adds up to seven and a half hours a month – that's one whole working day spent decluttering.

4. *Sell or donate any item of clothing you haven't worn for a year.* If you have just lost weight, throw out all your bigger clothes, so you're not allowed to pile it back on.

5. *Designate one place in the house for all incoming paper clutter,* otherwise it will spread all over the house. Also when you have to find something you can be certain that it's in the pile.

6. *Find a place for objects and put them back in their place after you've finished using them.* Store like with like. If something doesn't have a home it is more likely to get left any old place. Every day pick up five things and find a place for them. That's 150 things sorted in a month, 1,825 in a year.

7. *Don't just stuff things into drawers;* your clutter may be hidden from view but your mind knows that you've cheated. Place items you can't bear to part with in the attic in a box labelled "maybe" and review the situation in six months.

8. *Don't keep unwanted gifts,* especially ornaments. Sell them or give them away. Why surround yourself with other people's taste if it doesn't match your own?

9. *Throwing away,* giving away or selling is always a better option that buying more "storage solutions".

The 5 Whys is an effective way to get to the root cause of a problem; the technique is well known in business but it can also be applied to your own life challenges outside of the workplace. The technique was originally developed during the seventies by the father of the Japanese industrial revolution Sakichi Toyoda but it was made world famous when it was introduced into the Toyota Production System by Taiichi Ohno, who described the 5 Whys method as "the basis of Toyota's scientific approach . . . by repeating why five times, the nature of the problem as well as its solution becomes clear".

Its effectiveness lies in tracing cause and effect in sequence rather than relying on assumptions and logic traps. The answer to the fifth "Why" should reveal a broken process or an action or behaviour that needs to be modified. Sometimes it takes more than five whys to reach the root, and it is poorly suited to complicated multifaceted problems.

The example opposite demonstrates the critical process.

Problem: I'm not earning enough money through self-employment:

1 WHY? – PROJECTS TAKE LONGER THAN EXPECTED SO MY FEE BECOMES LESS VALUABLE

2 WHY? – BECAUSE I UNDERESTIMATE THE AMOUNT OF TIME I NEED TO COMPLETE THE PROJECT

3 WHY? – BECAUSE I FOCUS ON WHAT THE CUSTOMER WANTS RATHER THAN WHAT I CAN DELIVER

4 WHY? – BECAUSE I WANT TO PLEASE THE CUSTOMER AND DON'T WANT TO LOSE THE WORK BY ASKING FOR A MORE REALISTIC SCHEDULE

5 WHY? – BECAUSE I HAVE TO TAKE WHATEVER WORK COMES MY WAY

Solution: *I need to build longer lead times into my schedule for sourcing work contracts so I have greater choice*

Breaking down the problem in this cause/effect ladder can also reveal contradictions in your behaviour. Notice that the answer to the fourth why throws up an interesting paradox: "I want to please the customer" but the reality is that agreeing to an unrealistic deadline not only harms the bottom line but displeases the customer as well. So agreeing a longer deadline will benefit you and the customer. In this example the root cause of the problem of not earning enough turns out to be the need to devote more time to sourcing contracts.

PUT ON YOUR SIX

You've heard of the two expressions "put on your thinking cap" and "two heads are better than one" so when you want to address a decision from a variety of angles, why not put on six thinking caps? This tool was devised by the leading authority in the field of creative thinking, Edward de Bono, in his multi-million bestselling book, *Six Thinking Hats*®.

De Bono developed the method because he says, "the main difficulty of thinking is confusion. We try to do too much at once. Emotion, information, logic, hope and creativity all crowd in on us." Six thinking hats is "a very simple concept which allows a thinker to do one thing at a time." Its remarkable adaptability means "it can be taught with equal success to top-level executives and to pre-school children." It has been used in blue-chip companies throughout the world including NASA, IBM, DuPont, NTT (Japan), Shell, BP and Federal Express.

Each hat has a different style of thinking:

WHITE HAT – FACTS AND FIGURES

This thinking focuses on data and statements of facts, including information that is missing and needs to be researched or supplied. Analyse past trends and previous results.

RED HAT – EMOTIONS AND FEELINGS

The red hat views problems using intuition, emotion, gut feeling and aesthetic response. It also uses empathy to try to predict the feelings and reactions of other people. It is a good opportunity to express a preference between a series of available choices.

THINKING CAPS

BLACK HAT – CAUTIOUS AND CAREFUL

This hat is defensive and looks for risks, problems and obstacles. It highlights weak points and prevents mistakes and excesses. De Bono sees it as the most valuable of all the hats and the most used. It helps to counter too much yellow hat thinking.

YELLOW HAT – SPECULATIVE-POSITIVE

Wearing the yellow hat you think positively and overlook obstacles. You focus on all the benefits of a decision. It helps to raise morale and flagging spirits when the future looks tough. However, this is still an analytical process, not blind optimism.

GREEN HAT – CREATIVE THINKING

Green hat looks for creative solutions, alternative explanations and new possibilities, using blue sky thinking and free flow of ideas with no criticism or blocking. It is non-judgmental.

BLUE HAT – CONTROL OF THINKING

The blue hat takes the role of chairperson and stands for process control and directing what kind of thinking is being used so that it can be more productive. It looks for a summary of views and can call for activity from other hats.

FACE YOUR FEARS

Have you ever stopped to consider that you are living in the safest period of human history for the developed world? Life expectancy is double or triple what it used to be, and you don't have to worry about being eaten by a predator, starving to death or being clubbed by your neighbour. And yet we seem to live with more fear now than ever before. High achievers and people who consider themselves to be happy share a common trait – they face their fears and enjoy living outside their comfort zone.

If you are completely without fear you are either lying or insane. Some fears are healthy – people who aren't adrenaline junkies (that's most of us) derive no benefit from swimming in a crocodile-infested swap or trying to tightrope walk across the Grand Canyon. However, you should identify and confront the fears that are holding you back in life, the ones that will fill you with regret about missed opportunities when you are in your eighties.

We all have them and it takes courage to tackle them head-on, but the more you challenge yourself in this way the easier it gets. The main reason people fail is not through lack of trying or motivation or planning but through fear of failing (and sometimes fear of succeeding). What's worse still is when our fears hold other people back as well as ourselves.

It is helpful to think of fear as only being useful to protect you from danger in the present moment – such as jumping out of the path of a falling tree, or running away from a knife-wielding maniac. All other fears are projections into the future and do little to help you in the present.

1. FIND AN ALTERNATIVE. Often a fear is one of several possible scenarios, none of which are any more likely to happen. For example, you want to ask your boss for a raise, but fear prevents you. Why? Because you are afraid of the negative consequences – s/he says no and thinks you are greedy, you lose credibility and maybe even get fired. But are either of those outcomes any more likely to happen than s/he saying yes, or "not now, but here's what you need to do to get one" or you feeling good about yourself because you had the courage to ask?

2. IMAGINE THE WORST POSSIBLE OUTCOME and then look for a solution that will mitigate that worst case scenario or prevent it from happening.

3. MANY FEARS CAN BE TRACED TO AVOIDANCE OF BEING TOLD "NO". But actually fear is the biggest no-no because it stops us from even asking the question in the first place. How can you get what you need if you don't even ask for it?

4. IF YOU FEAR THAT BY ACTING YOU WILL STEP OVER SOME IMAGINED BOUNDARY OF ETIQUETTE, then consider whether what you ask produces value for that person; if it doesn't, find a way to produce value and you will conquer your fear of asking. For example, when asking your boss for a raise you could suggest taking on extra responsibilities.

5. DON'T WORRY ABOUT WHAT OTHER PEOPLE THINK. More damage is done to our public image by burying our fears than the mistakes we might make by acting in spite of them.

Whenever life acts we respond – cause and effect it would seem, but your reaction does depend on your attitude, which is under your sole control and no one else's.

What do you think is the most important word in the title above? If you chose "of" you're on the right track. We can't control everything that happens "in life" but we can control how we respond to it – our subjective personal experience "of life" is what really matters.

When bad events occur we need resilience to cope with them and that comes from our attitude. The more resilient you are, the happier you will be because your locus of well-being is not dependent on external events.

There are three ways that you can control your attitude – using emotion, thoughts and actions. Unfortunately most people allow their emotions to determine the other two, when in fact thoughts and actions are very effective at affecting emotions positively. Whenever you feel a strong negative emotion like anger or fear, use the "Thought stop" technique on page 124 to make you self-aware. Recognize that at this moment you need to focus on your thoughts and actions to take control of your negative emotions.

THE ROAD RAGE SCENARIO

Take road rage. Someone pulls into your lane without indicating and you have to brake hard to avoid a collision. You see red. The anger prevents you from thinking about safety or controlling your actions – you beep your horn, overtake on the inside lane and pull out in front of them, swearing and using threatening gestures. You have allowed your thoughts and actions to be controlled by your emotion. When you stop and say "No" to the anger, you allow your thoughts and actions to take control. You prioritize your safety and that of your passengers and other road users, make sure that the bad driver isn't causing any more hazards ahead, you turn on the radio to listen to some calming music.

There are many situations where we try to change the emotion only to make things worse. We turn to alcohol or drugs to block out the feelings, or try to change those around us, when we should be focusing on thoughts and actions, which are much easier to control than emotions. You create emotional resilience by changing what you think and what you do, which will affect your emotional state. Tackling your emotions head-on is like stubbornly driving a car with a flat tyre – anger and frustration don't get the tyre fixed, they just blind you to the inevitable and stop you taking action. Only your thoughts – "I'd better pull over and put on the spare" – and your actions – changing the tyre – fix the problem.

DO A SWOT Analysis

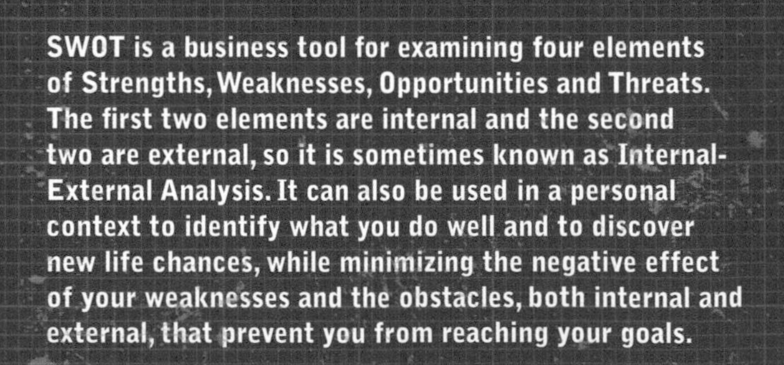

SWOT is a business tool for examining four elements of Strengths, Weaknesses, Opportunities and Threats. The first two elements are internal and the second two are external, so it is sometimes known as Internal-External Analysis. It can also be used in a personal context to identify what you do well and to discover new life chances, while minimizing the negative effect of your weaknesses and the obstacles, both internal and external, that prevent you from reaching your goals.

Do a SWOT analysis when you are in a good mood, otherwise you'll find it hard to come up with any strengths or unique qualities and you'll overplay your weaknesses. Take a large piece of paper, divide it into four quadrants and label each area with one of the four headings – this is your SWOT Matrix.

STRENGTHS >

1. What am I good at?
2. What do I do better than anyone else?
3. What do other people say that I'm good at?
4. What are my positive personal qualities?
5. What makes me unique and special?

Don't be shy about blowing your own trumpet, especially when answering the last question.

WEAKNESSES >

1. What am I bad at? [You may be wrong!]
2. What do other people say I'm bad at? [They may be wrong!]
3. What are my negative personal qualities?
4. What could I improve?
5. Which personal traits are holding me back?

Questions 4 and 5 are very important, because they offer the chance for change and growth. Notice that in questions 1 and 2, other people's perceptions of your weaknesses, may contradict your own view and you probably also have areas where you talk down your own abilities. Be honest and have the courage to face up to your weaknesses.

OPPORTUNITIES >

1. What are my goals, wishes and dreams?
2. Who can help me to achieve them?
3. What lifestyle changes would I like to make?
4. How can I improve my relationships?
5. How can I challenge myself?

When looking at opportunities, don't self-censor and block an idea or desire because you think it is unattainable. In other words, don't worry about the obstacles, you can deal with those in the next section. What would you wish for if attaining them wasn't an issue?

THREATS >

1. What stops me getting what I want/need?
2. Who stands in my way?
3. Do any of my weaknesses create obstacles?
4. What possible future threats do I need to plan for?
5. Which strengths could I use and weaknesses could I improve to overcome these threats?

Obstacles and threats create anxiety and sap your energy. Planning for them and drawing on your strengths spurs you into action and helps put you back in control.

Enhance your physical, emotional and spiritual well-being

CHANGE YOUR Breathing, CHANGE YOUR Mind

Osho tells the story of the time he challenged an athlete to try to imitate the actions of a child for eight hours. The child loved being copied and started doing many things – jumping, jogging, shouting, skipping. After four hours the child still had lots of energy but the athlete was exhausted.

Where did the child's energy come from? Osho says, "It comes from pranamaya kosha [vital life force]. A child breathes naturally, and of course breathes more prana in, more chi in, and accumulates it in his belly. The belly is the accumulating place, the reservoir. Watch a child; that is the right way to breathe. When a child breathes, his chest is completely unaffected. His belly goes up and down." Breathing from the belly highly oxygenates your system without building up tension in your chest; it also supports the breath so that your speaking and singing voice become expressive and authentic.

Actors and singers call this "centring and supporting the breath". Most of us breathe from the chest, especially when we are exercising. That's fine when you need to deliver oxygen quickly to your muscles, but if you do this all the time you build up tension in your chest and you won't use the full capacity of your lungs. When you root your breath in the lower abdomen you can enhance your physical, emotional and spiritual well-being, rather than just keep yourself alive.

CENTRING AND SUPPORTING THE BREATH

Lie on your back with your bare feet flat on the floor and your knees bent, shoulder-width apart, and pointing to the ceiling. Rest your head on a book so that you don't tilt the head back, pulling the neck out of line and creating tension in your throat. Allow your back and shoulders to lengthen and widen as they sink into the floor. There may be a small gap at the naturally curved base of your spine; more of this region will make contact with the floor as you relax, but don't force it. Rest your arms by your side, hands on your abdomen or place the backs of your hands on the side of your lower back so you can feel any movement there.

Gently turn your head from side to side to release neck tension. Spend a few minutes in this "semi-supine" position, allowing your body to make increasingly firm contact with the supporting ground.

Gradually slow the rate of breathing as it becomes deeper. This makes breathing more efficient and reduces the workload of your respiratory system – getting more oxygen and expelling more carbon dioxide for less muscle activity. It also helps to calm and focus the mind, increases lung capacity and efficiency and purifies the energy channels.

FOCUS ON YOUR BREATHING

Take a slow deep breath in through your nose and then sigh (without vocalizing) as you exhale. Breathe in slowly through your nose and then sigh noiselessly (i.e. don't engage your vocal cords) as you exhale. Release your stomach muscles so they spring back automatically to allow the breath to flow into your lungs effortlessly; try to imagine your lower back and abdomen opening to receive the air. Keep your upper chest relaxed and still, while all the activity takes place lower down. As you inhale notice your belly ballooning a little. It's harder to experience the expansive movement in your lumbar region as you inhale – it should flatten and lengthen as you inhale, round and shorten on the exhale.

Spend fifteen minutes breathing slowly and deeply and when you are ready roll gently onto your side and stand up. You should feel calm, relaxed and any pleasant tingling is a good sign of increased blood flow. The positive effects of your breathing should stay with you for several hours, keeping you calmer and more productive.

3 WAYS YOUR BRAIN TRICKS YOU

There's no doubting that our brains are amazing and complex, but as they try to make sense of the world, processing millions of bits of information per second, they can often lead us astray.

The most obvious examples of this are optical illusions – the visual relationship between colours and shapes, our sense of perspective or impossible staircases like the one in the movie *Inception* (invented in 1958 by British mathematical physicist Roger Penrose and developed soon after by artist Max Escher).

The most persistent and fundamental visual trick our brain plays on us every moment we are awake is compensating for the optical nerve blind spot. Look at the image at the top of the next page >

●   ✚

Place the image about 20 inches away, close your right eye and look at the cross with your left eye. Slowly move closer to the image (or move the image closer to you) as you continue to focus on the cross. At some point the dot will disappear and then reappear as you get even closer. Repeat the process, keeping your left eye closed and your right eye focused on the spot. This time the cross will disappear and reappear. The point where the image disappears is your blind spot, where there are no light receptors because that's where the optic nerve attaches to the retina. Your brain fills in what you should see by using the information from the other eye.

Avoid falling into self-limiting mind traps by reminding yourself daily that our experience of the world is subjective and that we might have a mistaken understanding about reality. *Here are three other ways our brains can fool us:*

1 MEMORIES ARE FLUID AND UNRELIABLE

We tend to think of memories as like photos of an event, but research by neuroscientist Karim Nader, psychologist Elizabeth Loftus and others shows that the very act of remembering can change our memories. Memories are not fixed because emotions felt when we recall an event can reshape them. A famous example of this is that thousands of people confidently remember watching footage on September 11 of the first plane hitting the north tower of the World Trade Center. But footage of the first plane aired for the first time the following day. A 2003 study of 569 college students found that 73 per cent shared this misperception. Even George Bush has reported seeing the first plane crash that day. Just because we are confident about our memory does not mean we are always accurate.

2 INATTENTION BLINDNESS

It is possible to see something important without observing it. Our brains filter most of the input that reaches our senses; they have to, or we could never focus on anything. However, the dangers of this selective attention have been highlighted by researchers Daniel Simons and Christopher Chabris. Before you read further, take this short selective attention test:

www.youtube.com/watch?v=vJG698U2Mvo

Simons warns that "we instinctively believe that the mechanism of attention will automatically bring to focus things that matter to us. And it turns out that this intuition is dangerously wrong." It is the same reason why the most common kind of accident between cars and motorcycles is a car pulling out of a junction into the path of the motorbike – the car driver fails to observe the unexpected even when it is clearly in their line of vision.

3 CHANGE BLINDNESS

Simons and Chabris conducted another classic experiment showing that "people fail to notice surprisingly large changes to their visual world when those changes occur during a brief moment of distraction". Subjects were approached by a stranger asking for directions. After ten seconds two people carrying a wooden door passed between them, during which the stranger was replaced by someone else. Half of the subjects continued giving directions with no idea they were talking to someone else.

Simons warns that, "we think that we see, notice, and remember far more than we actually do . . . the goal here is we have to teach ourselves to counter intuitions in those cases where they are likely to lead us astray".

For more information on this subject view Simons' TED talk on counter-intuition at www.youtube.comwatch?v=eb4TM19DYDY or read The Invisible Gorilla: And Other Ways Our Intuitions Deceive Us by Daniel Simons and Christopher Chabris

MAKE EXERCISING SELF-CONTROL ENJOYABLE

A study by Juliano Laran (University of Miami) and Chris Janiszewski (University of Florida, Gainesville) published in the *Journal of Consumer Research* in 2010 has found that "Self-control failures depend on whether people see activities involving self-control (e.g., eating in moderate quantities) as an obligation to work or an opportunity to have fun."

That sounds like common sense – going on a diet is easier to stomach when we associate it with fun rather than hard work. But that is precisely where the power of this finding lies – high self-control depends on how we reference that activity. If you focus on denial and "work" you are less likely to succeed that if you set up the exercise in your mind as inherently "fun".

In the experiment participants were asked to hold a sweet between their fingers and take it in and out of their mouths. Then a packet of sweets was left on their desk while they performed unrelated surveys, with no instructions as to whether or not they should eat. "We found that participants who are usually high in self-control perceived the initial candy task – which involved touching, but not eating Skittles and M&Ms – as an opportunity to have fun (they were playing with candy) . . . Participants who are usually low in self-control, however, perceived the initial candy task as an obligation to work."

In a similar study people with low and high self-control had equal success with self-control success when the word "fun" was used in the instructions for the task. "These results show that low self-control people can be made to act like high self-control people and show regulatory success if tasks that involve exerting self-control are framed in a way that people will perceive it as fun and not work."

So, if you want to increase your self-control, you are more likely to succeed if you persuade yourself that you are going to have fun, and that the experience is rewarding and enjoyable than if you focus on self-denial and hard work (unless asceticism gives you a considerable amount of pleasure).

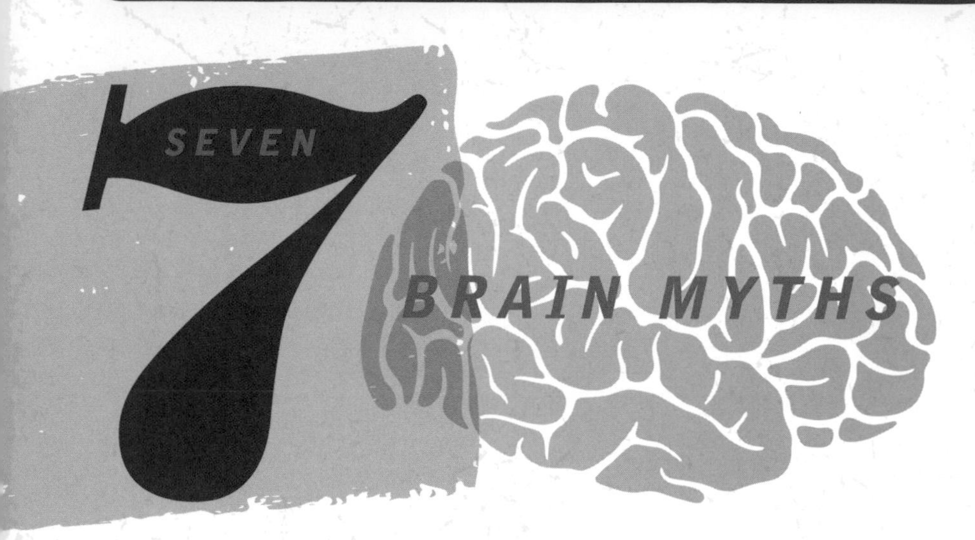

During the last decade neuroscientists have learned more about cognition and the human brain than they have during the last hundred, but despite this many myths about the brain persist in popular culture.

1 THE BRAIN DEVELOPS FIXED FUNCTIONS EARLY

"Ten years ago most neuroscientists saw the brain as a kind of computer, developing fixed functions early," says Michael Merzenich of the University of California, San Francisco, a pioneer in the field of brain plasticity. "What we now appreciate is that the brain is continually revising itself throughout life."

2 OUR INTELLIGENCE AND BEHAVIOUR IS FIXED BY OUR GENES

There is a genetic component to the way our brains are wired when we are born, but the plasticity of the brain means that the brain evolves physically throughout our lives. In *The Mismeasure of Man*, a key book in debunking IQ as defined and innate, Steven Jay Gould says "Flexibility is the hallmark of human evolution . . .

In other mammals, exploration, play and flexibility of behaviour are qualities of juveniles, only rarely of adults. We retain not only the anatomical stamp of childhood, but its mental flexibility as well . . . Humans are learning animals." Even Richard Dawkins is hopeful about our ability to break free from our genetic programming. In *The Selfish Gene,* talking about altruism he says, "We are built as gene machines and cultured as meme machines, but we have the power to turn against our creators. We, alone on earth, can rebel against the tyranny of the selfish replicators."

3 BRAIN DECLINE WITH AGE IS INEVITABLE

If you engage your brain every day in stimulating activities that are fun, varied, challenging and new, take moderate exercise, eat a healthy diet, and have regular social interaction, there is no reason why you should experience the mental decline that we used to associate with old age. In some cases it can even be reversed. Research shows that healthy people with increased mental stimulation reduce their risk of Alzheimer's and other forms of dementia by half. "If you get strict about it, you see that the decline occurs not as a function of age, but with the onset of disease," reports John C. Morris, MD, Co-Director of the Alzheimer's Disease Research Center at Washington University School of Medicine.

4 ALCOHOL KILLS BRAIN CELLS

Alcohol damages brain function but does not kill brain cells. The damage occurs to the mechanism by which brain cells communicate with each other because the ends of the neurons, the dendrites, become degraded. Severe alcoholics develop a neurological disorder called Wernicke-Korsakoff syndrome, in which neurons in part of the brain die, but this is because the alcohol interferes with the body's ability to absorb an essential B-vitamin called thiamine. Thiamine is often prescribed during the treatment of alcoholism, especially during the initial withdrawal period.

5 WE ONLY USE TEN PER CENT OF OUR BRAIN

Common sense and knowledge of natural selection should tell you that this is nonsense, otherwise there would be lots of examples of people with brain injuries with no loss of brain function, and we would have developed smaller brains, since they require twenty per cent of the body's nutrients. Every part of the brain has a function, and while certain areas of the brain show increased neurological activity during certain tasks, the whole brain is involved all the time, even during sleep. It can be a useful metaphor to motivate you to use more of your potential, but it isn't literally true, so any life coach or self-help guru who peddles this myth is being disingenuous.

6 THE BIGGER THE BRAIN THE SMARTER YOU ARE

There is no correlation between the size of a person's head or brain and their intelligence. However, if you develop a particular talent in music, art or sport, etc, you will generate brain changes in certain brain areas, and have a different brain structure. For example, it has been found that the brains of highly trained meditators have certain areas of their cortex that are thicker than those of average people.

7 THE BRAIN DOESN'T GROW NEW CELLS

It was once thought that your body stops producing brain cells after a certain age and then they die off throughout your adult life, but this is not true. Numerous studies have shown that neurogenesis continues throughout a person's life and there are several things you can do to encourage the growth of new brain cells (see page 78). The millions of cells that die every year is minute compared to the billions that remain.

"READING, AFTER A CERTAIN AGE, DIVERTS THE MIND TOO MUCH FROM ITS CREATIVE PURSUITS. ANY MAN WHO READS TOO MUCH AND USES HIS OWN BRAIN TOO LITTLE FALLS INTO LAZY HABITS OF THINKING."

ALBERT EINSTEIN

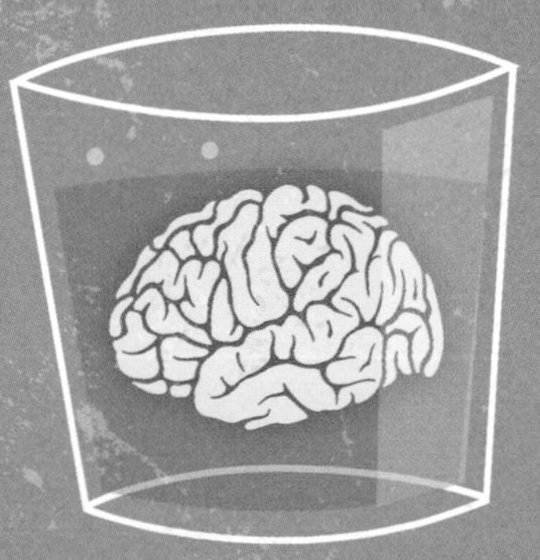

Now close this book, open your mind and go create!

MICHAEL POWELL

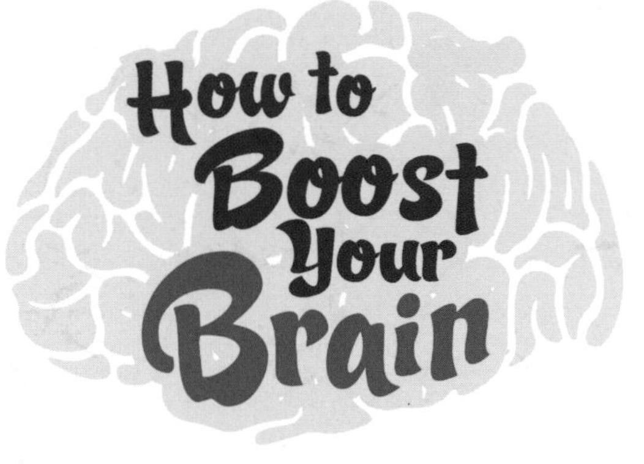
How to
Boost
Your
Brain